The History of Hymn Singing as told through

One Hundred & One Famous Hymns

Edited by
Mary Ann Thorson

With special thanks to the eminent hymnologist
The Reverend Leonard Ellinwood, Ph. D.
for his scholarly critique prior to publication,
and to W. Thomas Smith, Executive Director of
The Hymn Society of America.

The History of Hymn Singing as told through

One Hundred & One Famous Hymns

by Charles Johnson

HALLBERG PUBLISHING CORPORATION
Book Publishers — ISBN 0-87319
Delavan, Wisconsin 53115

Published by The Reader's Digest Association, Inc., with
the permission of HALLBERG PUBLISHING CORPORATION.
ISBN Number 0-87319-021-1
Library of Congress Catalog Card No. 82-83452
Manufactured in the U.S.A. First printing October 1982.

The History of Hymn Singing as told through

One Hundred & One Famous Hymns

is dedicated to those thousands

of Christians throughout

the United States who participated

in their selection.

May this precious volume help

preserve our rich heritage.

Contents

Our story begins with hymn singing at the time of Jesus and progresses in historical order: Catholic hymns and Gregorian chant; the followers of John Huss who are today referred to as Brethren and Moravians; to the evangelical hymns of Martin Luther and the quite different views of his contemporary, John Calvin.

Baptist hymn singing is told through the life of John Bunyan (Pilgrim's Progress); the Congregational through Isaac Watts the "Father of English hymnody", and the Episcopal through the hymns of many famous Anglican hymn writers.

Methodists will learn not only of the tremendous contribution John and Charles Wesley made to hymn singing but also of the founding of their denomination. (as will Lutherans, Calvinists, Congregationalists and others.)

Beginning on page 134 are found our favorite Sunday school songs and the famous gospel hymns. Through the biographies of these writers you will learn of the development of Sunday schools and of the great evangelical crusades.

The Last Supper

Jesus and His disciples as depicted by Leonardo Da Vinci in his famous painting of "The Last Supper" after which, as *Matthew 26:30* records, "And when they had sung an hymn, they went out into the mount of Olives"

ome, walk with us through the streets of Bethlehem and Jerusalem during the time of Jesus. Religion was taught orally and to help people memorize, much of it was written as poetry and sung. In the great Temple at Jerusalem we hear beautiful, elaborate music. The Temple priests and choirs chant the psalms and portions of the Pentateuch as we in the congregation listen. Later at the synagogue in Bethlehem, we in the congregation sing the psalms to tunes taught and preserved by oral tradition.

Journeying quickly through the next three hundred years we see the early Christians supplement the Hebrew Psalter with songs and poems of their Christian experiences. As the Christian church spread westward through the Roman Empire the early Greek hymns and New Testament Canticles gradually change to Latin.

Following the Edict of Milan (313), Christianity became the religion of the Empire. In 374, Aurelius Ambrose, Bishop of Milan ushered in a great era of singing which lasted three hundred years, earning for him the title, "Father of Latin hymnody". It was Ambrose who taught the Western church to glorify the Triune God in sacred song and encouraged all of the people to participate.

The Lord's Prayer

Jesus; as recorded in Matthew 6:9-13

William Lester

POPE GREGORY I

540 - 604

Gregory the Great became Pope in 590 and in fourteen short years instituted liturgical and musical reforms which lasted fourteen hundred years.

What the world soon came to know as Gregorian chant, resulted from Pope Gregory's determination to present the world with one uniform and universal Church. A new school of music was founded in Rome. The music was slow, uniform, without rhythm and sung in unison much like the earlier recitative method of psalm singing. Gregory adopted it and sent singers to all Church centers in Europe to teach the new style of singing. The reforms instituted by Gregory were carried out with exactness. No deviations were allowed. Congregational hymn singing virtually ceased because the new Gregorian chants required trained choirs and clergy to sing them correctly.

Gregory did however allow the singing of Latin hymns on special occasions and wrote many beautiful Latin hymns himself. The Christmas hymn, *O Come, O Come Emmanuel*, is a fine example of the hymns which were allowed. Written in the 600's it was one of seven songs sung at vespers on successive days between December 17th and 23rd. And now, after thirteen hundred years, it is still one of our most loved Christmas hymns.

Gradually the worship service of the Church took distinct form and three lyric portions of the Nativity became a lasting part of Church service. Luke 1:46 became the *Magnificat*. Luke 1:68 became the *Benedictus* and Luke 2:29-31 the *Nunc Dimittis*.

12th Century Gregorian Chant

To the four scales of the Ambrosian system, Pope Gregory added four *plagal* (oblique) scales, and each type of Gregorian chant was assigned one of these eight official church scales (modes.)

The above Gregorian chant was used on Sundays throughout the year. This example, sent to us from St. Mary's College, Notre Dame, IN., dates from the 12th century. Prior to that time only the spaces and not the lines were used for notes.

Gregorian chant is one of the great achievements of our Western heritage - fourteen hundred years of pure melodic music.

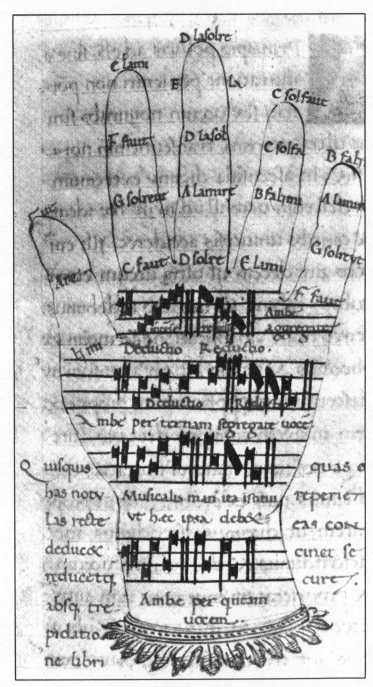

The Guidonian Hand

Each joint represented a different syllable and tone, and a new scale began on every fourth tone. In this manner an instructor could teach melodies fairly quickly by holding up his left hand and pointing to various joints.

Guido of Arezzo, 995 to 1050, established a six note scale and associated each note with the Latin syllables still used today, *ut, re, mi, fa, sol, la*. He also invented the four line staff using both the lines and spaces to give a definite place on the staff to each sound. His system of musical notation finally solved the almost impossible task of accurately writing down sound and timing on paper.

O Come, O Come, Emmanuel

tr. Neale [1851]

15th Century
French Processionale

1. O come, O come, Em - man - u - el, And ran-som cap - tive Is - ra - el, That mourns in lone - ly ex - ile here Un - til the Son of God ap - pear. Re - joice! re - joice! Em-man - u - el Shall come to thee, O Is - ra - el!

2. O come, Thou Rod of Jes - se, free Thine own from Sa - tan's tyr - an - ny; From depths of hell Thy peo - ple save And give them vic - tory o'er the grave. Re - joice! re - joice! Em-man - u - el Shall come to thee, O Is - ra - el!

3. O come, Thou Day-spring, come and cheer Our spir - its by Thine ad - vent here; And drive a - way the shades of night, And pierce the clouds and bring us light! Re - joice! re - joice! Em-man - u - el Shall come to thee, O Is - ra - el!

4. O come, Thou Key of Da - vid, come, And o - pen wide our heaven - ly home; Make safe the way that leads on high, And close the path to mis - er - y. Re - joice! re - joice! Em-man - u - el Shall come to thee, O Is - ra - el! A-MEN.

All Glory, Laud, and Honor

Theodulph of Orleans, cir. 760-821　　　　　　　*Melchior Teschner, 1585-1635*

Refrain　tr. Neale [1851]

1. All glo - ry, laud, and hon - or To thee, Re - deem - er, King;
To whom the lips of chil - dren Made sweet ho - san - nas ring.

Stanzas 2, 3, 4, 5, and 6.

2. Thou art the King of Is - rael, Thou Da - vid's roy - al Son,

Repeat refrain

Who in the Lord's Name com - est, The King and Bless - ed One!

3 The company of angels
　Are praising thee on high,
　And mortal men and all things
　　Created make reply. *Refrain.*

4 The people of the Hebrews
　With palms before thee went;
　Our praise and prayer and anthems
　　Before thee we present. *Refrain.*

5 To thee before thy Passion
　They sang their hymns of praise;
　To thee, now high exalted,
　　Our melody we raise. *Refrain.*

6 Thou didst accept their praises;
　Accept the prayers we bring,
　Who in all good delightest,
　　Thou good and gracious King. *Refrain.*

According to legend this celebrated Palm Sunday hymn was composed over eleven hundred years ago by Bishop Theodulph while he was imprisoned. When Louis I heard it sung, he immediately ordered Theodulph freed.

Beautiful Savior! King of Creation

Anonymous

Tr. Joseph Augustus Seiss

Silesian Folksong

1. Beau - ti - ful Sav - ior! King of cre - a - tion! Son of
2. Fair are the mead-ows, Fair are the wood-lands, Robed in
3. Fair is the sun - shine, Fair is the moon-light, Bright the
4. Beau - ti - ful Sav - ior! Lord of the na - tions! Son of

God and Son of Man! Tru - ly I'd love Thee, Tru - ly I'd
flow'rs of bloom - ing spring; Je - sus is fair - er, Je - sus is
spar - kling stars on high; Je - sus shines bright - er, Je - sus shines
God and Son of Man! Glo - ry and hon - or, Praise, ad - o -

serve Thee, Light of my soul, my Joy, my Crown.
pur - er; He makes our sor - rowing spir - its sing.
pur - er Than all the an - gels in the sky.
ra - tion, Now and for - ev - er - more be Thine! A - MEN.

In time, the strong desire of people to sing hymns in their own language could not be stilled, particularly in Germany, and beloved hymns as *Beautiful Savior! King of Creation* were written in German by anonymous German priests and sung on festive occasions.

15

JOHN HUSS

1369 - 1415

John Huss was born in Husinec, Bohemia, and educated at the University of Praha. He was ordained a priest in 1401 and named Dean of Philosophy at that university. The following year he was named Rector.

Huss became a follower of English reformer John Wycliffe whose writings he translated and circulated throughout Bohemia. On July 6th, 1415 the Council of Constance found John Huss guilty of heresy. He was burned at the stake and his ashes thrown into the Rhine river. His followers went underground and began a movement they called "The Hidden Seed".

Over the years Huss's followers were known as Hussites, Bohemian Brethren, Moravian Brethren and Brethren. They were a spirited group and loved to sing hymns. In 1501 they published the first collection of hymns written in the vernacular on the European continent.

Persecuted and ridiculed for their religious zeal many members of the Moravian Brethren fled in 1730 to the large estate of Count von Zinzendorf. Here, under the protection of the Count the little band of refugees established a religious colony they called Herrnhut. True to their tradition they immediately began work on a hymnal which they published in 1735.

Also in 1735 a group of Moravians came to America landing at Savannah, Georgia and enroute taught their hymns to John and Charles Wesley and other members of the Oxford Holy Club (Methodists). In 1740 they left Savannah and established settlements at Philadelphia and Bethlehem in Pennsylvania, and at Winston-Salem in North Carolina. As expected they wasted no time in publishng a hymnal. Just seven years after landing in America their first hymnal was published in Germantown, Pennsylvania.

Jesus Makes My Heart Rejoice

Henriette Luise von Hayn, 1724-1783

"Herrnhuter Choralbuch", 1735

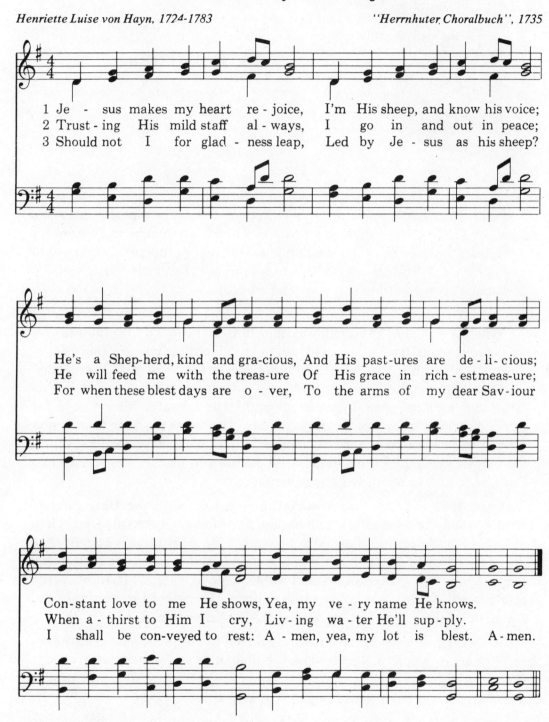

1 Je - sus makes my heart re - joice, I'm His sheep, and know his voice;
2 Trust - ing His mild staff al - ways, I go in and out in peace;
3 Should not I for glad - ness leap, Led by Je - sus as his sheep?

He's a Shep-herd, kind and gra-cious, And His past-ures are de - li - cious;
He will feed me with the treas-ure Of His grace in rich - est meas-ure;
For when these blest days are o - ver, To the arms of my dear Sav-iour

Con-stant love to me He shows, Yea, my ve - ry name He knows.
When a - thirst to Him I cry, Liv - ing wa - ter He'll sup-ply.
I shall be con-veyed to rest: A - men, yea, my lot is blest. A - men.

17

MARTIN LUTHER

November 10, 1483 - February 18, 1546

Martin Luther was born at Eisleben, Germany, shortly after his family moved there from Mohra where they had been farmers for generations. While an infant the family moved again, this time to Mansfeld where his father Hans got a job as a copper miner. Later his father became foreman of two smelting furnaces and as years went by he attained civic prestige and prosperity.

When of school age Martin was sent to Latin school by his father, who was determined that he should get a good education. At the age of fourteen his father sent him to Magdeburg to the most highly regarded school, where he continued his studies in Latin, Greek and Hebrew. As his father did not have enough money to pay Martin's board, Martin sang for his food at the windows of wealthy citizens. The following year Martin was sent to Eisenach to continue his studies and stayed there for four years. Once again he sang for his bread until one day an elderly woman, Ursula Citta, took him in and gave him a home.

From 1501 to 1505 Luther worked his way through the University of Erfurt where he studied law and obtained a Master of Arts degree. Then in July of 1505, on the road near Stotternheim, Martin was caught in a thunderstorm. When a bolt of lightning just missed him, he cried out to the family Saint, "Help me Saint Ann. I will become a monk." Martin was true to his word. Against the wishes of his father, he entered the order of the Augustinian Eremites and on April 4, 1507 was ordained.

In October of 1508 Luther was transferred to the prestigious University of Wittenberg where he lectured on the dialectics and physics of Aristotle. Four years later, at the age of 29, Luther was admitted to the faculty of Theology at Wittenberg and began teaching Bible.

It was on October 31, 1517 that Martin Luther hurled his challenge to the Church establishment, nailing his Ninety-five Theses concerning indulgences to the door of the Castle Church at Wittenberg. The issue was joined. The Reformation was begun. (Continued on page 20.)

The Castle Church, Wittenberg, Germany

This is the Castle Church at Wittenberg where, in 1517, Luther nailed his Ninety-five Theses concerning indulgences (selling remission of punishment for sins) to the church door. And where for the rest of Luther's life he was protected by the knights and armies of the Electors of Saxony, Frederick the Wise and later his brother, John the Steadfast, as well as many German princes of surrounding principalities.

The Wartburg Castle

Condemned by the Edict of Worms (1521) to be burned at the stake as a heretic, Luther was "kidnapped" by knights of Frederick the Wise, Elector of Saxony, and spirited away to one of Saxony's most impregnable castles, Wartburg. Here, disguised as the knight, Junker Jorg, Luther lived from May 1521 until February 1522 and translated the New Testament into German.

(Luther, continued from page 18.)

During the next twenty-nine years Luther became immensely popular with the German people. Not only did he lead the scholarly fight for theological and Church reforms, he gave the German people a Bible they could read (the New Testament in 1521, the Old Testament in 1534), wrote a German Catechism and published German hymnals.

Luther was one of the few hymn writers who also composed the music for many of his hymns. He began writing hymns in 1523, when he wrote *Out Of The Depths I Cry To Thee.* Luther's first hymnal of eight hymns (of which he wrote four) was published in 1524. It was so popular a second edition was published later that year containing twenty-five hymns, eighteen of which Luther wrote.

In the preface to the *Spiritual Hymn Booklet,* Luther wrote:

"That the singing of spiritual hymns is a goodly thing and pleasing to God, I do not think is hidden from any Christian, since everyone is aware not only of the example of the kings and prophets in the Old Testament (who praised God with singing and playing, with poesy and all manner of string music), but also of the universality of this custom in Christendom from the beginning . . .".

Luther's great hymn, *A Mighty Fortress Is Our God,* was written in 1529 shortly after the Diet of Spires, when German princes made formal protest against revoking some of their liberties and received the name protestants.

The hymn quickly became the battle hymn of the Reformation, inspiring people during the Reformation period and throughout the Thirty Years War between Catholics and Protestants, that racked Germany from 1618 to 1648. (Continued on page 22.)

A Mighty Fortress Is Our God

Martin Luther   *Martin Luther*

1. A might-y for-tress is our God, A bul-wark nev-er fail-ing;
2. Did we in our own strength con-fide, Our striv-ing would be los-ing;
3. And though this world, with dev-ils filled, Should threat-en to un-do us,
4. That word a-bove all earth-ly powers, No thanks to them, a-bid-eth;

Our help-er He, a-mid the flood Of mor-tal ills pre-vail-ing:
Were not the right Man on our side, The Man of God's own choos-ing:
We will not fear, for God hath willed His truth to tri-umph through us:
The Spir-it and the gifts are ours Through Him who with us sid-eth:

For still our an-cient foe Doth seek to work us woe; His craft and power are great,
Dost ask who that may be? Christ Je-sus, it is He; Lord Sa-ba-oth, His name,
The Prince of Dark-ness grim—We trem-ble not for him; His rage we can 'en-dure,
Let goods and kin-dred go, This mor-tal life al-so; The bod-y they may kill:

And, armed with cru-el hate, On earth is not his e-qual.
From age to age the same, And He must win the bat-tle.
For lo, his doom is sure, One lit-tle word shall fell him
God's truth a-bid-eth still, His king-dom is for-ev-er. A-MEN.

Luther House In Wittenberg

The monastery of the Augustinian Eremites at Wittenberg later became known as Luther House. Here Luther lived, lectured, and labored from 1508 to 1546. The property was presented to him in 1525 by Elector Frederick the Wise. To the right of the tower were the family rooms and his study; to the left were the large and small lecture halls. Today, Luther House is a depository for the writings and mementos of the history of the Reformation.

(Luther, continued from page 20.)

When in 1529 Luther published his new hymnal, it replaced his earlier hymnals and was quickly put to use in his Wittenberg church where he had retained the Catholic form of mass, adding only a sermon and his beloved hymn singing.

During his career Luther wrote a total of thirty-seven hymns. The last hymnal he supervised was published in 1545. It contained one hundred and twenty hymns and ninety-seven hymn tunes.

It is said that at the time of the Diet of Augsburg (1530) Luther gathered the people in the Castle (Coburg) about him and said, "Come, let us defy the devil", whereupon he lead the singing of *Out Of The Depths I Cry To Thee.* In 1546 the people of Halle again sang this hymn. This time with tears in their eyes as Luther's coffin passed through the city on its way to its final resting place in Wittenberg.

Like the Reformation, the spirit of Luther and Luther's evangelical hymns carried on, under new leaders, inspiring men and nations.

Out Of The Depths I Cry To Thee

Martin Luther   *Strassburg Kirchenampt, 1525*

1. Out of the depths I cry to thee, O Lord, my sins be-wail - ing!
Bow down thy gra-cious ear to me, Make thou my prayer a - vail - ing.

Mark not my mis-deeds in thy book, But on my sins in

mer - cy look, Or who can stand be - fore thee? A-men.

2 With thee there is forgiveness, Lord,
   And love and grace abounding;
The noblest thought and deed and word
   Were else but empty sounding.
      All guilty in thy sight appear;
      All to thy presence come in fear,
   And find thy lovingkindness.

3 Like those who watch upon the wall
   To welcome in the morning,
My soul doth wait thy quiet call,
   Her self with hope adorning.
      So may all Israel look for thee,
      And in thy day find mercy free,
   And plenteous redemption. Amen.

JOHN CALVIN

July 10, 1509 - May 27, 1564

The singing of metrical versions of the Psalms appeared in the 1540's, largely through the efforts of John Calvin.

Born at Noyon in Picardy, France, John Calvin received his early education in Paris. Later he studied at the universities of Orleans, Bourges and Paris, first for the priesthood and then for the legal profession. Dissatisfied with the teachings of the Roman Catholic Church, Calvin in 1532 allied himself with the cause of the Reformation, publishing in 1536 the first edition of his monumental theological work, *The Institutes Of The Christian Religion.*

The persecution of the Protestants in France caused Calvin to flee and when visiting Geneva in 1536, his friend evangelist William Farel convinced him to stay. With Farel, Calvin transformed Geneva's government into a virtual theocracy. A Protestant confession of faith was adopted by the city council and made binding on all citizens. Then in April of 1538, the Council ordered Farel and Calvin to leave the city because they refused to use unleavened bread in Holy Communion.

Calvin went to Strassburg, Germany, where he took charge of a church of French refugees, taught, wrote, and with Clement Marot published one of the first metrical psalters in 1539. This small volume contained eighteen metrical psalms, twelve of which were by Marot and five by Calvin. Recalled to Geneva in September of 1541, Calvin took this French Psalter with him and over the next twenty-one years he enlarged and improved it, in numerous editions.

Calvin became the acknowledged head of Geneva in 1541 and through its theocratic government directed all religious, social and political affairs. Many people in Western Europe thought of Geneva as the Protestant Rome. The power of Calvin's government was absolute and Calvin's influence reached far beyond Geneva. Through his writings, his Church, College and Academy, Calvin had great influence in Holland and France. And when Reverend John Knox, a fervent admirer of Calvin, returned to Scotland from his years of exile in Geneva (with his Psalter published in Geneva in 1556 and the English Geneva Bible), Calvin's influence spread throughout Scotland and England.

Cathedral Of St. Pierre, Geneva

John Calvin's church, the Cathedral of St. Pierre, Geneva, Switzerland, was begun in the 10th century on the site of an ancient temple and completed in the 13th century. In 1536 Calvin made it his principal church and it remains to this day an important, historic, Presbyterian/Reformed church center.

John Calvin's order of church worship was unpretentious. It consisted of prayer, preaching and singing in union, strict metrical translations of the Psalms without musical accompaniment. Calvin's theological concepts were also much different than Luther's as indicated by the "Calvinists" Westminster Confession of 1647 which states: (1) God as sovereign both foreordains and foreknows all things, including man's destiny; and (2) those predestined to salvation will be saved as it is impossible for the elect to fall away from grace.

In 1562, Calvin published his famous *Genevan Psalter,* the popularity of which was largely due to the music of Louis Bourgeois, music editor and cantor at St. Pierre Church. The *Genevan Psalter* soon spread throughout Europe and colonial America, popularizing the idea of singing metrical versions of the *Psalms.* In America versions of the *Genevan Psalter,* by various compilers, accompanied the Hugenot immigrants to South Carolina and Florida in 1565, Sir Francis Drake to California in 1579, the Jamestown settlers in 1607, the Puritans at Cambridge in 1617, and the Pilgrims in 1620. When the *Mayflower* sailed for America the community the Pilgrims sought to found was based on the *Genevan Bible* of 1560 and the *Ainsworth Psalter* of 1612, which was a combination of popular French and Dutch "Calvinist" psalters.

All People That
On Earth Do Dwell
"Calvin's Reformation Hymn"

The hymn, *All People That On Earth Do Dwell*, was suggested to us by the McCormick Theological Seminary as expressing Calvin's and Presbyterian/Reformed hymn concepts in much the same way as *A Mighty Fortress Is Our God* could be said to represent Luther's.

The following excerpts from the Handbook to the Hymnal (1935 Presbyterian) clearly state this hymn's position to Presbyterian hymnody and Calvin's firm convictions regarding church music.

"Author William Kethe was a native of Scotland but the time and place of his birth are lost in obscurity. He fled before the persecution of Mary in 1555-1558 and found refuge in Geneva.

Hymn - This well-known version of Psalm 100 is the only hymn of Kethe's in common use. It is taken from the "Psalter" published in 1561 by that enterprising printer John Day who suffered much for his loyalty to the reformed faith.

This version, composed by Kethe, who was a faithful friend of John Knox has resisted many proposed alterations and in its quaintness and rugged diction calls us to praise with practically the same idioms as well as the same tune known to the original group of Presbyterians at Geneva. This hymn expresses the dominant motive of the entire hymnal ...

Composer Louis Bourgeois was born in Paris. An adherent of John Calvin, he was invited to Geneva, in 1541, to teach and organize the music of the Church. He was appointed cantor in one of the churches at Geneva, and later, 1545, master of the choristers. He was admitted to the rights of citizenship in consideration of his being a respectable man and willing to teach children.'

In his work he was highly successful, and congregational singing in Geneva was an inspiring experience. However, he was a man of some independence and was thrown into prison for having, without permission, altered several tunes of the psalms. Through Calvin's intervention he was released on the following day. Bourgeois left Geneva in 1557, and probably died in Paris."

All People That On Earth Do Dwell

Psalm c. Rev. William Kethe, 1561

Old Hundredth
Louis Bourgeois, 1551
[English form of final line]

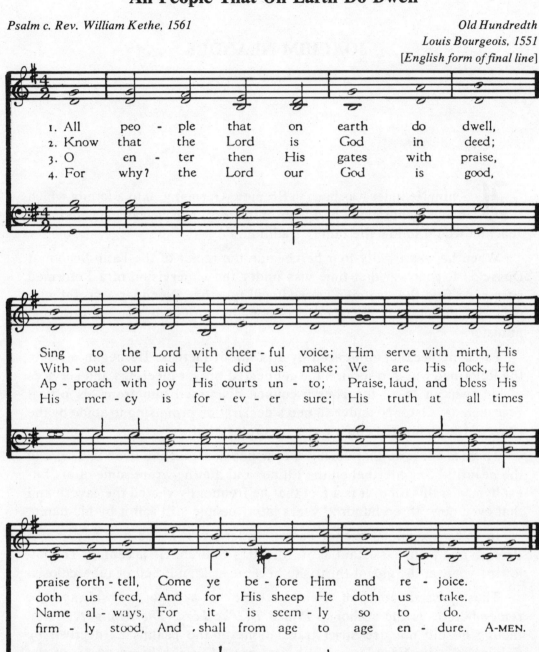

1. All   peo - ple that   on   earth   do   dwell,
2. Know that   the   Lord   is   God   in   deed;
3. O   en - ter   then   His   gates with praise,
4. For   why?   the   Lord   our   God   is   good,

Sing   to   the   Lord with cheer - ful voice; Him serve with mirth, His
With - out our   aid   He   did   us   make; We   are   His flock, He
Ap - proach with joy   His courts un - to; Praise, laud, and bless His
His   mer - cy   is   for - ev - er sure; His truth at   all   times

praise forth - tell, Come ye   be - fore Him and   re - joice.
doth   us   feed, And   for   His sheep He   doth   us   take.
Name al - ways, For   it   is   seem - ly   so   to   do.
firm - ly stood, And shall from age to   age   en - dure. A-MEN.

27

JOACHIM NEANDER

1650 - May 31, 1680

Joachim Neander was born in Bremen, Germany, into a family which for four generations had been ministers and it was expected that Joachim would follow the family tradition.

When he was twenty-four he became the rector of the Latin School at Dusseldorf, which at that time was under the supervision of a Reformed pastor. At first the two men worked well together. Neander assisted with pastorial duties and preached occasionally, although not an ordained minister.

Later he became influenced by a group of Pietists. He began missing the Reformed worship service and conducted prayer meetings and services of his own. In 1676 the church council dismissed him from his office. Fourteen days later Neander signed a declaration promising to abide by the rules of the Reformed church and was reinstated.

There is a legend that during the suspension Joachim lived in a cave in the beautiful Neanderthal on the Rhine and that he wrote some of his finest hymns at this time. It is a fact that he frequently visited the cavern and that even now, three hundred years later, people still call it by his name.

In 1679 Joachim's friend, Pastor Under-Eyck asked him to come to Bremen and be his assistant at St. Martin's Church. He accepted. The following year, at the age of thirty, he became sick and died of tuberculosis.

Thus passed Joachim Neander, the man who will always be remembered as the author of *Praise To The Lord, The Almighty.* Even though he did not use strict translations of the psalms as decreed by Calvin, Joachim Neander was the first great German hymn writer of the Reformed (Calvinistic) faith.

Praise To The Lord

Joachim Neander, 1650-1680
Tr. Catherine Winkworth, 1827-1878, alt.

"Stralsund Gesangbuch," 1665

1 Praise to the Lord, the Al - might - y, the King of cre - a - tion!
2 Praise to the Lord, who o'er all things so won-drous-ly reign - eth,
3 Praise to the Lord, who doth pros-per thy work and de - fend thee;
4 Praise to the Lord! O let all that is in me a - dore him!

O my soul, praise him, for he is thy health and sal - va - tion!
Shel-ters thee un - der his wings, yea, so gen-tly sus - tain - eth!
Sure-ly his good-ness and mer - cy here dai-ly at - tend thee.
All that hath life and breath, come now with prais - es be - fore him.

All ye who hear, Now to his tem - ple draw near;
Hast thou not seen How thy de - sires e'er have been
Pon - der a - new What the Al - might - y can do,
Let the A - men Sound from his peo - ple a - gain:

Join me in glad ad - o - ra - tion!
Grant-ed in what he or - dain - eth?
If with his love he be - friend thee.
Glad - ly for aye we a - dore him. A - men.

29

JOHN BUNYAN

November 30, 1628 - August 31, 1688

Although his great hymn from *Pilgrim's Progress* was not set to music until two hundred years later, the books and powerful sermons of this great Baptist leader had a tremendous influence throughout the English speaking world of the mid-1600's.

John Bunyan was born in the town of Elstow, near Bedford, England. His father was a tinker (repairer of pots and pans). He attended the school in Elstow and, at sixteen, was drafted into the Parliamentary Army.

After his discharge he worked at his father's trade. It is said that at the time of his marriage his wife's only dowry was two books and that they had "neither a spoon nor a dish". After the Bunyans became members of the small Baptist church at Bedford he was asked to become their pastor. John accepted saying, "I wish to mend people's souls as well as their pots and pans".

Like the Anabaptists before him, John Bunyan revolted against Roman Catholicism and the established Church of England and quickly became a leader among the Nonconformists and Dissenters, a leadership for which he spent ninety days in the Bedford jail in 1650 for the crime of preaching.

Upon release, Bunyan immediately resumed his powerful sermons. In 1660 he was arrested again. This time he was sentenced to twelve years in prison and during those years he wrote nine books.

Released in 1672, the undaunted John Bunyan resumed preaching and as expected found himself sentenced again in 1675. This time for only six months. While in jail Bunyan began writing his epic *Pilgrim's Progress,* which sold one hundred thousand copies in the ten years following its publication, influencing literate Englishmen everywhere.

At a time when the General Baptists were debating whether any congregational singing should be allowed, John Bunyan along with Benjamin Keach, pastor of the Particular Baptist Church in Southwark, (who instituted hymn singing in 1673) was a powerful advocate of congregational (Continued on top of page 32.)

30

He Who Would Valiant Be

John Bunyan

English Traditional Melody
arr. R. Vaughn Williams [1906]

He who would val - iant be Let him come hi ther;
Who so be - set him round With dis - mal sto - ries,
Hob - gob - lin, nor foul Fiend, Can daunt his Spir - it;

One here will Con - stant be, Come Wind, come Wea — ther.
Do but them - selves con-found, His strength the more is.
He knows, he at the end, Shall Life In — her — it.

There's no dis - cour - age - ment Shall make him once re - lent
No Lyon can him fri —ght, He'll with a Gy — ant Fight,
Then Fan — cies fly a — way, He'll fear not what men say,

His first a - vowed in - tent To be a pil - grim.
But he will have a — right, To be a pil - grim.
He'll la — bor Night and Day, To be a pil - grim.

(John Bunyan's biography continued from page 30.)

hymn singing. Bunyan spoke of it as being a "divine institution", whereas Keach quoted from Matthew 26:30 to prove that singing praise to God was not sinful and Keach's son carried the same argument to Baptists in America.

In later years John Bunyan was often referred to as Bishop Bunyan attesting to his profound influence on the early development of the Baptist and other Nonconformist groups and in the development of the Baptist's love of congregational singing.

In 1688, John Bunyan died in London following exposure in the rain while on an errand to help an alienated father and son.

AMERICA'S FIRST BOOK

Few issues in the early 1600's were more controversial than congregational singing. As the controversy raged between and within groups America's first book was published, *The Bay Psalm Book,* which by 1698 not only combined psalms and hymns in the same book but also included melodious tunes to which to sing them. In the preface, the Puritans resolved the conflict by stating:

"There have been three questions especially stirring concerning singing. First, what psalmes are to be sung in churches. Whether David's and other scripture psalmes or the psalmes invented by the gift of godly men in every age of the church. Secondly, if Scripture Psalmes, whether in their own words or in such meeter as English poetry is wont to run in. Thirdly, by whom are they to be sung? Whether by the whole churches together with their voices? Or by one man singing alone and the rest joining in silence, and in the close singing amen."

In Answer:
". . . there are many verses together in several psalmes of David which run in rithmes . . . which shows at least the lawfulness of singing psalmes in English rithmes."

The press on which *The Bay Psalm Book* was printed was procured from England in January 1639 by Reverend Jesse Glover for Harvard College. When Reverend Glover died, his wife married Reverend Henry Dunster, the first President of Harvard, and the press was in his house until 1665.

The initial printing, in 1640, was not fully approved and a revised version of *The Bay Psalm Book* was ordered in 1650. It was widely accepted, passing through seventy editions in America, England and Scotland.

Title-Page of

THE BAY PSALM BOOK

Ninth Edition

The First Edition Having Music

1698

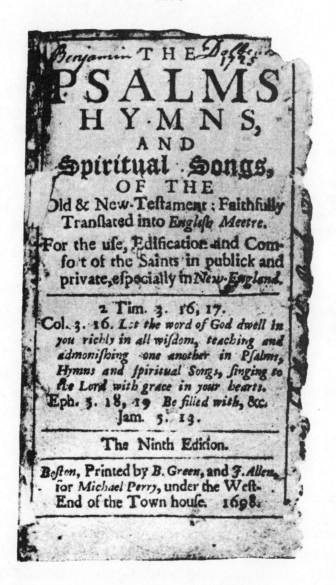

In 1947 a copy of this book
sold for $151,000.

ISAAC WATTS

July 17, 1674 - November 25, 1748

Isaac Watts, the "Father of English hymnody", was born in Southampton, England, the first of nine children. His father was a taylor and deacon at the Above Bar Congregational Church and was imprisoned several times for his religious beliefs. Isaac's mother of French Huguenot descent used to carry young Isaac to visit his father in jail.

Isaac was educated at the free school in Southampton where he learned Greek, Latin and Hebrew and in the Nonconformist academy of Thomas Rowe at Stoke Newington, near London.

In 1699, he became assistant pastor of Mark Lane Independent Chapel, London. And, in 1702, its pastor. Watts resigned in 1712 due to a serious illness and went to the home of Sir Thomas Abney as tutor and chaplain to the household. Of frail health, he remained with the Abney family until he died in 1748.

Although Isaac Watts wrote sixty books on a wide range of subjects (his book on logic was used as a textbook at Oxford University), he gained worldwide renown for writing "New Testament" hymns.

Watts was convinced that the song of the New Testament Church should express the gospel of the New Testament, whether in psalm versions or in hymns. He also held that the song should express the thoughts of those Christians who sung them.

It was the New Testament hymn of Isaac Watts that helped bridge the gap between the Calvinist psalms and the Lutheran hymns and set Christians in England and America singing.

Between 1705 and 1748, Watts wrote six hundred hymns, many of which are still favorites, as evidenced by the three hymns of Watts selected for this collection of 101 famous hymns.

34

When I Survey The Wondrous Cross

Isaac Watts

Isaac B. Woodbury, 1819-1858

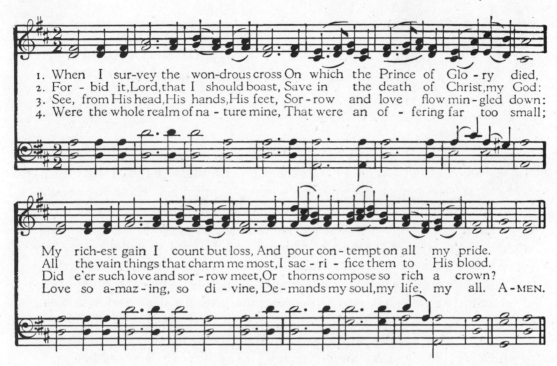

1. When I sur-vey the won-drous cross On which the Prince of Glo - ry died,
2. For - bid it,Lord,that I should boast, Save in the death of Christ,my God:
3. See, from His head,His hands,His feet, Sor - row and love flow min-gled down:
4. Were the whole realm of na - ture mine, That were an of - fering far too small;

My rich-est gain I count but loss, And pour con-tempt on all my pride.
All the vain things that charm me most,I sac - ri - fice them to His blood.
Did e'er such love and sor - row meet,Or thorns compose so rich a crown?
Love so a-maz-ing, so di - vine, De-mands my soul,my life, my all. A-MEN.

O God, Our Help In Ages Past

Isaac Watts

Probably by William Croft, 1678-1727

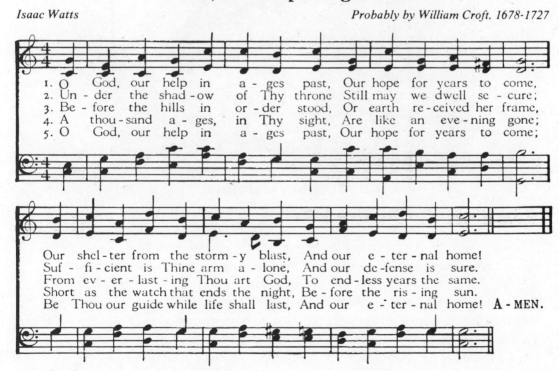

1. O God, our help in a - ges past, Our hope for years to come,
2. Un - der the shad - ow of Thy throne Still may we dwell se - cure;
3. Be - fore the hills in or - der stood, Or earth re - ceived her frame,
4. A thou-sand a - ges, in Thy sight, Are like an eve - ning gone;
5. O God, our help in a - ges past, Our hope for years to come;

Our shel - ter from the storm - y blast, And our e - ter - nal home!
Suf - fi - cient is Thine arm a - lone, And our de - fense is sure.
From ev - er - last - ing Thou art God, To end - less years the same.
Short as the watch that ends the night, Be - fore the ris - ing sun.
Be Thou our guide while life shall last, And our e - ter - nal home! A - MEN.

GEORGE FREDERICK HANDEL

February 23, 1685 - April 14, 1759

Born in Halle, Germany, George studied music at the Halle Cathedral. He began his music career playing in a Hamburg opera orchestra. He went to Italy and winning acclaim for his work, moved on to England in 1713. He enjoyed great success as an operatic composer and entrepreneur. By 1737 his luck changed and Handel was bankrupt. He turned to church music. It was then that he wrote his immortal *Messiah*, and Handel's star burned brighter than ever before. Although he became blind at the age of sixty-seven, he continued his musical performances. Before he died in 1759 George Handel created forty-six operas, thirty-two oratorios, many cantatas and scores of smaller works, including the music to which we sing Isaac Watt's hymn *Joy To The World! The Lord Is Come.*

Old Meeting, Uxbridge
One of England's Oldest Congregational Churches
Established in 1662.   Drawing 1716

Even though the Congregational Movement (the belief that each local church should govern itself, write its own Creed and determine its own worship service) began in England in the late 1500's, its adherents, which numbered over one thousand clergymen, did not separate from the Church of England until 1662 when the *Act of Uniformity* forced episcopal ordination and acceptance of the Prayer Book as a basis of worship. It was due to the Act of Uniformity and similar laws that young Isaac Watts' father was jailed on several occasions for being a Deacon of the Above The Bar Congregational Church.

Joy to the World!

JOHN

June 17, 1703 - March 2, 1791

CHARLES

December 18, 1707 - March 29, 1788

THE WESLEYS

Charles Wesley, the poet of Methodism, was the eighteenth of nineteen children born to the distinguished Anglican minister Reverend Samuel Wesley and his wife Susanna.

Born at Epworth, Lincolnshire, England, Charles with his brother John (who was three years older) were destined to have a profound effect upon the world in which we live.

Both Charles and John were educated at Oxford. John was ordained a priest in the Church of England in 1728. In 1729 he returned to Oxford as a tutor while Charles was at Oxford studying for his M.A. degree.

At Oxford, the brothers with George Whitefield formed the Oxford Holy Club to counter prevailing attitudes. Its members were expected to follow a disciplined approach to Bible study, worship, communion and visitation to the sick and imprisoned. Because of their methodical practice of religious concepts the members of the Holy Club were soon referred to as Methodists by fellow students.

Charles obtained his M.A. from Oxford in 1732 and in 1735 was ordained a deacon and elder in the Church of England. Later in 1735 thirteen members of the Holy Club (including John and Charles) set sail for Savannah, Georgia, where they planned to work as missionaries. Aboard ship they met a group of Moravians and John Wesley became so interested in their hymn singing he began to study German, making translations of their German hymns for his group of "Methodists".

Charles returned to England in 1736 and John followed two years later. Back in England, both Charles and John became friends of the Moravian leader Count von Zinzendorf. In 1738 each had dynamic personal conver-
(Continued on page 40.)

O For A Thousand Tongues

Charles Wesley

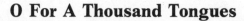

Carl G. Glaser, 1784-1829
Arr. by Lowell Mason

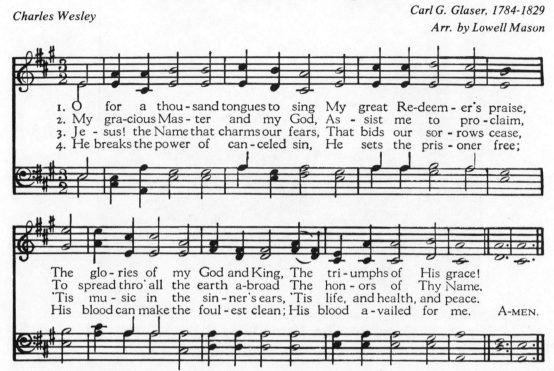

1. O for a thou-sand tongues to sing My great Re-deem-er's praise,
2. My gra-cious Mas-ter and my God, As-sist me to pro-claim,
3. Je-sus! the Name that charms our fears, That bids our sor-rows cease,
4. He breaks the power of can-celed sin, He sets the pris-oner free;

The glo-ries of my God and King, The tri-umphs of His grace!
To spread thro' all the earth a-broad The hon-ors of Thy Name.
'Tis mu-sic in the sin-ner's ears, 'Tis life, and health, and peace.
His blood can make the foul-est clean; His blood a-vailed for me. A-MEN.

5 He speaks, and, listening to His voice,
  New life the dead receive;
  The mournful, broken hearts rejoice;
  The humble poor believe.

6 Hear Him, ye deaf; His praise, ye dumb,
  Your loosened tongues employ;
  Ye blind, behold your Saviour come;
  And leap, ye lame, for joy.

The Hymn Of The Methodists

With the exception of one edition, *O For A Thousand Tongues* has always been the first hymn in the Methodist hymnal. Charles Wesley wrote this hymn in 1739 to celebrate the first anniversary of his spiritual rebirth. It was published in his *Hymns and Sacred Poems*, 1740. The original poem had eighteen stanzas, of which the seventh through the twelfth became known as the most loved hymn, *O For A Thousand Tongues*. In some collections other stanzas are sung.

Charles Wesley wrote the following about his conversion in his Journal:

"Sunday, May 21, 1738 . . . At nine my brother and some friends came and sang a hymn to the Holy Ghost . . . In about half an hour they went. I betook myself to prayer . . . Still I felt a violent opposition and reluctance to believe; yet still the Spirit of God strove with my own and the evil spirit till by degrees He chased away the darkness of my unbelief. I found myself convinced, I knew not how nor when, and immediately fell to intercession."

The biography of Lowell Mason, the composer who arranged this music for *O For A Thousand Tongues,* appears on page 100.

The New Room In The Horsefair, Bristol, England

The first Methodist meeting house, established 1739.

(The Wesleys, continued from page 38.)

sion experiences and full of evangelical zeal, they set about to proclaim the message of Jesus to England, Ireland and Wales. John was the organizing genius, preacher and driving force while Charles gave the movement the wings of music and developed its practical theology in his hymns.

At a time when the Calvinistic belief in salvation of only an ''elect'' was widely held, the hymns of Charles and John Wesley loudly proclaimed the unlimited atonement of Jesus. It is said that the word ''all'' must have had a special place in Charles Wesley's vocabulary for it appears so frequently in his hymns.

In March of 1739 evangelist George Whitefield persuaded John Wesley to carry on his ministry to the coal miners of Bristol, England, while he returned to the Colonies. John had never before conducted open air services and wrote:

''I could scarce reconcile myself to his strange way of preaching in the fields . . . having been all my life so tenacious of every point relating to decency and order that I should have thought the saving of souls almost a sin if it had not been done in a church''.

(Continued on page 42.)

Jesus, Lover Of My Soul

Charles Wesley   *John Bacchus Dykes*

1. Je - sus, Lov - er of my soul, Let me to thy bos - om fly,
2. Oth - er ref - uge have I none; Hangs my help - less soul on thee;

While the near - er wa - ters roll, While the tem - pest still is high;
Leave, ah, leave me not a - lone, Still sup - port and com - fort me.

Hide me, O my Sav - iour, hide, Till the storm of life is past;
All my trust on thee is stayed, All my help from thee I bring;

Safe in - to the ha - ven guide, O re - ceive my soul at last.
Cov - er my de - fense - less head With the shad - ow of thy wing. A - men.

3 Thou, O Christ, art all I want;
   More than all in thee I find.
Raise the fallen, cheer the faint,
   Heal the sick, and lead the blind.
Just and holy is thy Name,
   I am all unrighteousness;
False and full of sin I am,
   Thou art full of truth and grace.

4 Plenteous grace with thee is found,
   Grace to cover all my sin;
Let the healing streams abound,
   Make and keep me pure within.
Thou of life the fountain art,
   Freely let me take of thee;
Spring thou up within my heart,
   Rise to all eternity. Amen.

*Composer John Bacchus Dykes' biography appears on page 76.

The Foundery, London, England

The second Methodist meeting house established, The Foundery in London soon became the Methodist's main headquarters. (1739 - 1778)

(The Wesleys, continued from page 40.)

Thus began on April 2nd, 1739, the first of thousands of Wesley's "revival" meetings to be held in the fields before the multitudes who thronged to hear him.

In his journal for May 9, 1739 John wrote that he purchased a piece of ground "near St. James churchyard in the Horsefair" on which to build a room large enough to contain the societies of Nicholas Street and Baldwin Street and on May 12th the first stone was laid.

This building, the first Methodist meeting house, still stands today in Bristol, England and although it's official name is now Wesley's Chapel, Broadmead, it is still known as The New Room in the Horsefair. The building was licensed for public worship October 17, 1748, the first to take advantage of the *Toleration Act* (1689). Charles Wesley was furious, saying "I protest against this needless, useless, senseless license . . . We are not Dissenters . . . We are active members of the Church of England." Charles settled in Bristol in 1749 and married Sarah Gwynne. In 1771 they moved to London.

Shortly after the property in Bristol was purchased the need for a London headquarters also became evident and later, in 1739, John leased a dilapidated cannon foundery that had not been used since an explosion in 1716 all but demolished it. Out of this "vast heap of ruins" he made a chapel, which could accommodate fifteen hundred people, a smaller meeting room for groups up to three hundred and a book room. John also established on these premises services similar to those in Bristol, a free dispensary, a free school for sixty pupils, an alms house for widows and private apartments for visiting preachers. (Continued on page 44.)

Christ The Lord Is Risen Today

14th century Latin
tr. Charles Wesley

From Lyra Davidica, 1708

1. Christ the Lord is risen to-day, Al - - - le - lu - ia!
2. Lives a-gain our glo-rious King, Al - - - le - lu - ia!
3. Love's re-deem-ing work is done, Al - - - le - lu - ia!
4. Soar we now where Christ has led, Al - - - le - lu - ia!

Sons of men and an-gels say, Al - - le - lu - ia!
Where, O death, is now thy sting? Al - - le - lu - ia!
Fought the fight, the bat-tle won, Al - - le - lu - ia!
Fol-lowing our ex-alt-ed Head, Al - - le - lu - ia!

Raise your joys and tri-umphs high, Al - - le - lu - ia!
Once He died, our souls to save, Al - - le - lu - ia!
Death in vain for-bids Him rise, Al - - le - lu - ia!
Made like Him, like Him we rise, Al - - le - lu - ia!

Sing, ye heavens, and earth re-ply, Al - le - lu - ia!
Where's thy vic-tory, boast-ing grave? Al - le - lu - ia!
Christ hath o-pened par-a-dise, Al - le - lu - ia!
Ours the cross, the grave, the skies, Al - le - lu - ia! A-men.

John Wesley Chapel, London

The Mother Church of World Methodism built to John Wesley's design in 1778, and remains to this day, a most important Methodist center.

(The Wesleys, continued from page 42.)

In 1777 it was decided to erect a new Wesley Chapel on a site near The Foundry. On November 1st, 1778 the new chapel, built to John Wesley's design, was opened by him and stands today as the Mother Church of World Methodism.

Although both John and Charles traveled extensively preaching, John set the record, over 200,000 miles on horseback, preaching more than 40,000 sermons during his sixty-three year ministry.

Throughout their lives Charles and John worked closely together. Their only real difference of opinion came as the movement grew too large for them to recruit enough Anglican (Church of England) ordained ministers. It was then that Charles took exception to John's practice of allowing. other preachers to give communion, to John's ordaining of ministers and to permitting Methodist services at the same time as local Anglican church services.

During his life Charles wrote some six thousand five hundred hymns giving wings to the Methodist movement. John, the brilliant organizer, was also a good musician and superb music editor. The hymnals they published had worldwide effect, for at a time when many churches were discussing whether or not to permit singing and Calvinists said only the elect were saved, Charles wrote hymns declaring salvation for all and

(Continued on page 46.)

44

O Come, All Ye Faithful

Anonymous. Latin, 18th century   *Source unknown, 18th century melody*

1. O come, all ye faith-ful, joy-ful and tri-um-phant, O come ye, O
2. Sing, choirs of an-gels, sing in ex-ul-ta-tion, O sing, all ye
3. Yea, Lord, we greet Thee, born this hap-py morn-ing, Je-sus, to

come ye to Beth-le-hem! Come and be-hold Him, born the King of
cit-i-zens of heav'n a-bove! Glo-ry to God, all glo-ry in the
Thee be all glo-ry giv'n; Word of the Fa-ther, now in flesh ap-

REFRAIN

an-gels! O come, let us a-dore Him, O come, let us a-dore Him,
high-est!
pear-ing!

O come, let us a-dore Him, Christ, the Lord! A-MEN.

The words and music to this most loved hymn are now considered
to have been written by John Francis Wade in about 1740.

(The Wesleys, continued from page 44.)

John wrote, for example, in his preface to their hymnal *Sacred Melody*, these instructions for hymn leaders:

1. Learn these tunes before you learn any other.

2. Sing them exactly as printed here . . . if you have learned to sing them otherwise, unlearn it . . .

3. Sing all. See that you join with the congregation . . .

4. Sing lustily and with good courage. Beware of singing as if you were dead or half asleep. . .

5. Sing modestly. Do not bawl so as to be heard above or distinct from the congregation.

6. Sing in time. Whatever time is sung, be sure and keep with it. Do not run before nor stay behind but attend close to the leading voices . . . take care not to sing too slow.

7. Above all sing spiritually. Have an eye to God in every word you sing. Aim at pleasing *Him* more than yourself . . . to do this attend strictly to the sense of what you sing and see that your heart is not carried away by the sound but offered to God . . .

And thus, the methods of Methodists eventually reached out influencing the world.

JAKOB LUDWIG FELIX MENDELSSOHN

February 3, 1809 - November 4, 1847

Felix Mendelssohn, composer of the music to which we sing Wesley's *Hark, The Herald Angels Sing*, was born in Hamburg, Germany, the son of a Jewish banker and grandson of the prominent Jewish philosopher Moses Mendelssohn

In 1811 the French occupied Hamburg and the family fled to Berlin, where they joined the Lutheran church and added the name Bartholdy to indicate that they had become Christians.

Felix, by the age of twelve, composed five symphonies. When twenty years old he began a four year world-wide tour and became a great favorite in England. The revival of interest in the compositions of Bach was largely due to this influence. At the age of thirty-six, Felix Mendelssohn settled in Leipzig, Germany. Only thirty-eight when he died, Mendelssohn none-the-less produced immortal oratorios and built the Gewandhaus Orchestra of Leipzig into the first of the great modern symphony orchestras.

Hark, the Herald Angels Sing

Charles Wesley

Felix Mendelssohn-Bartholdy
Arr. by William S. Cummings

1. Hark! the her - ald an - gels sing, "Glo - ry to the new - born King:
2. Christ, by high - est heaven a - dored; Christ, the Ev - er - last - ing Lord!
3. Hail the heav,en-born Prince of Peace! Hail the Sun of Right-eous - ness!

Peace on earth, and mer - cy mild, God and sin - ners rec - on-ciled!"
Late in time be - hold Him come, Off - spring of the Vir-gin's womb:
Light and life to all He brings, Risen with heal - ing in His wings.

Joy - ful, all ye na - tions, rise, Join the tri - umph of the skies;
Veiled in flesh the God - head see; Hail th' In-car - nate De - i - ty,
Mild 'He lays His glo - ry by, Born that man no more may die,

With th' an - gel - ic host pro-claim, "Christ is born in Beth - le - hem!"
Pleased as man with men to dwell, Je - sus, our Em-man-u - el.
Born to raise the sons of earth, Born to give them sec - ond birth.

Hark! the her - ald an - gels sing, "Glo - ry to the new-born King." A - MEN.

JOHN NEWTON

July 24, 1725 - December 21, 1807

John Newton grew up on the decks of a sailing ship. His mother died when he was but seven years old. At age eleven he went to sea on his father's ship making five voyages to the Mediterranean. When war seemed imminent, he was drafted into the Royal Navy. He deserted ship, was captured, flogged at the mast and degraded. Dismissed from the service, John joined the crew of a slave trading ship. Later John Newton became a captain and plied the seas for six years, carrying his cargoes of slaves.

Newton was restless and having read Thomas A. Kempis' *The Imitation Of Christ* sought out the "Dissenters". In 1754 he left the sea, settled down with his devoted wife, Mary Catlett, and worked as a tide surveyor in Liverpool. Here he became closely associated with Whitefield and the Wesleys while studying the scriptures in Hebrew and Greek and occasionally preaching.

In 1764 he was ordained in the Church of England and appointed curate of Olney where he formed a friendship with the poet William Cowper and together they wrote the famous hymn book, the *Olney Hymns,* published in 1779. It contained three hundred forty-seven hymns of which Cowper wrote sixty-six and Newton over two hundred and eighty.

In 1780 Newton became vicar at St. Mary Woolnoth, London, and continued to preach almost until his death. In poor health and almost blind friends advised him to retire but he replied, "What, shall the old African blasphemer stop while he can speak!".

Amazing Grace

John Newton

Early American melody

1. A - maz - ing grace! how sweet the sound, That saved a wretch like me!
2. 'Twas grace that taught my heart to fear, And grace my fears re - lieved;
3. Thro' man - y dan - gers, toils, and snares, I have al - read - y come;
4. The Lord has prom - ised good to me, His word my hope se - cures;

I once was lost, but now am found, Was blind, but now I see.
How pre - cious did that grace ap - pear The hour I first be - lieved!
'Tis grace hath bro't me safe thus far, And grace will lead me home.
He will my shield and por - tion be As long as life en - dures. A-MEN.

John Newton is buried in St. Mary's churchyard and the epitaph which he wrote reads:

John Newton
Once an infidel and libertine,
A servant of slaves in Africa:
Was by the rich mercy of our Lord and Saviour, Jesus Christ
Preserved, restored, pardoned,
And appointed to preach the Faith
He had laboured long to destroy.
Near sixteen years at Olney in Bucks;
And twenty-seven years in this church.

FRANZ JOSEPH HAYDN

March 31, 1732 - May 31, 1809

Born in Rohrau, Austria, the son of a wheelwright, Franz Joseph Haydn became one of the world's great concert composers and is today regarded as the "Father of the Symphony". At the age of eight, Franz was sent to the Roman Catholic school of St. Stephen's in Vienna. His musical genius was evident even as a child.

In 1761, at the age of twenty-nine, he became musical director to the Hungarian family of Esterhazy. Their palace had its own chapel, theater and concert room for which Haydn had full charge, plus an orchestra, choir and soloists to render his compositions.

For thirty years creating new musical masterpieces for the palace of Esterhazy was both a joy and a necessity for Haydn. In music and in conversation Haydn cheered people by his happy touches of Croatian peasant humor and religious feeling.

When in 1797 Haydn visited England, Oxford University conferred upon him honorary Doctorate of Music degree and he enjoyed great success among the nobility and royalty.

During his illustrious career Haydn wrote over one hundred symphonies, twenty-two operas, four oratorios and an untold amount of chamber music. The music to which we sing John Newton's hymn, *Glorious Things Of Thee Are Spoken,* was originally written by Haydn as a national anthem and was first sung in 1797 on the birthday of Emperor Franz II.

Glorious Things of Thee Are Spoken

John Newton

Franz Joseph Haydn

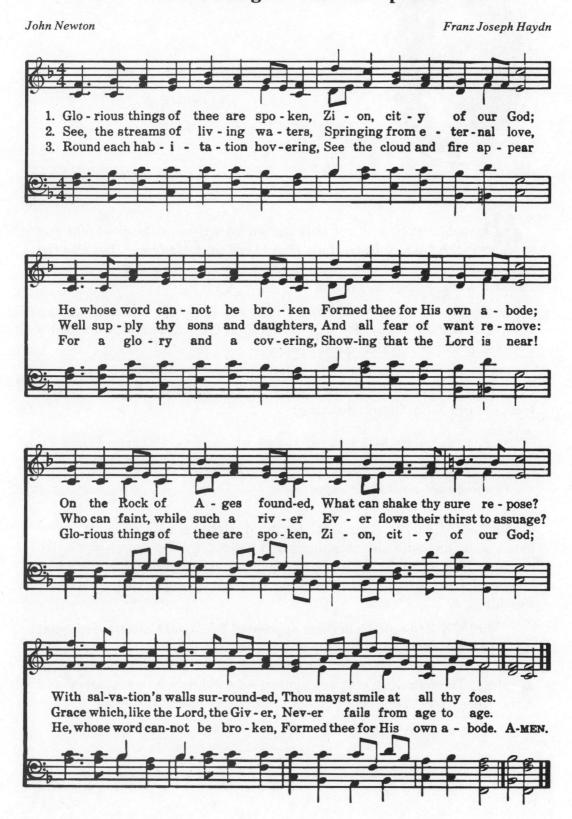

1. Glo - rious things of thee are spo - ken, Zi - on, cit - y of our God;
2. See, the streams of liv - ing wa - ters, Springing from e - ter - nal love,
3. Round each hab - i - ta - tion hov - ering, See the cloud and fire ap - pear

He whose word can - not be bro - ken Formed thee for His own a - bode;
Well sup - ply thy sons and daughters, And all fear of want re - move:
For a glo - ry and a cov - ering, Show-ing that the Lord is near!

On the Rock of A - ges found-ed, What can shake thy sure re - pose?
Who can faint, while such a riv - er Ev - er flows their thirst to assuage?
Glo-rious things of thee are spo - ken, Zi - on, cit - y of our God;

With sal-va-tion's walls sur-round-ed, Thou mayst smile at all thy foes.
Grace which, like the Lord, the Giv - er, Nev-er fails from age to age.
He, whose word can-not be bro - ken, Formed thee for His own a - bode. A-MEN.

REGINALD HEBER

April 21, 1783 - April 3, 1826

Reginald Heber was not only the gifted writer of the beautiful and powerful hymn, *Holy, Holy, Holy! Lord God Almighty!* but also the first to compile a hymnal in which the hymns were selected and organized for each week in the church year.

Reginald was born at Malpas, Cheshire, England, the scion of an ancient Yorkshire family. He was educated at Oxford where he formed a friendship with Sir Walter Scott.

Following his ordination as an Anglican priest, Heber was assigned to the parish at Hodnet for sixteen years. It was while serving this parish, Heber wrote John Thornton saying:

"My psalm-singing continues bad. Can you tell me where I can purchase Cowper's *Olney Hymns,* with the music, and in a smaller size, without the music to put in the seats? Some of them I admire much, and any novelty is likely to become a favorite, and draw more people to join in the singing."

Unable to locate the hymnals he wanted, Heber set out to create a new hymn book, one with singable tunes and divided by the church week. He completed his hymnal in 1820, but it was not published because the Archbishop of London thought "the time was not ripe for such a book of worship".

In 1822 Reginald Heber was appointed Bishop of Calcutta. He spent three years working in India. Then, on April 3rd, 1826, while in Trichinopoly to confirm a class of forty-two converts, he died suddenly of apoplexy. The following year his hymnal was published in his honor and *Holy, Holy, Holy! Lord God Almighty,* became known worldwide.

Holy, Holy, Holy!

Reginald Heber

John B. Dykes

1. Ho-ly, ho-ly, ho - ly! Lord God Al-might - y! Ear - ly in the
2. Ho-ly, ho-ly, ho - ly! all the saints a - dore Thee, Cast - ing down their
3. Ho-ly, ho-ly, ho - ly! though the dark-ness hide Thee, Though the eye of
4. Ho-ly, ho-ly, ho - ly! Lord God Al-might - y! All Thy works shall

morn - ing our song shall rise to Thee; Ho - ly, ho - ly, ho ly,
gold - en crowns a - round the glass - y sea; Cher-u - bim and ser - a - phim
sin - ful man Thy glo - ry may not see; On - ly Thou art ho - ly;
praise Thy Name, in earth, and sky, and sea; Ho - ly, ho - ly, ho - ly,

mer-ci - ful and might-y! God in Three Per-sons, bless-ed Trin - i - ty.
fall-ing down be-fore Thee, Which wert, and art, and ev - er-more shalt be.
there is none be-side Thee, Per - fect in power, in love, and pu - ri - ty.
mer-ci - ful and might-y! God in Three Per-sons, bless-ed Trin - i - ty! A - men.

The biography of John Bacchus Dykes, composer of the music to which
we sing *Holy, Holy, Holy!*, appears on page 76.

FELICE de GIARDINI

April 12, 1716 - June 8, 1796

Felice de Giardini was born in Turin, Italy. As a young man he became a chorister at the Cathedral of Milan and studied violin under G.E. Somis and voice under Paladini.

In his twenties he played in various opera houses and orchestras in Rome and Naples. In 1748, Giardini toured Italy and Germany and in 1750, toured England giving concerts. Widely acclaimed, he returned to London in 1752 and stayed until 1784. For thirty-two years Felice de Giardini was recognized as the impresario of the Italian Opera group in London, a violinist, teacher, and conductor of the first rank.

In 1769, Lady Huntingdon asked Giardini to write four hymn tunes for a hymnal being made by Martin Madan called, *A Collection Of Psalms And Hymn Tunes Sung At The Chapel Of The Lock Hospital.*

Of these four tunes, the one since named the Italian hymn came to be sung with the lyric poem *Come Thou Almighty King,* published anonymously twelve years earlier.

In 1796, Giardini went to Moscow but died less than three months after giving his initial concert.

Come, Thou Almighty King

Authorship uncertain
Whitefield's Collection, 1757 a.

Felice de Giardini

1. Come, thou al-might-y King, Help us thy Name to sing,
2. Come, thou In-car-nate Word, Gird on thy might-y sword;

Help us to praise! Fa-ther all glo-ri-ous, O'er all vic-
Our prayer at-tend; Come and thy peo-ple bless, And give thy

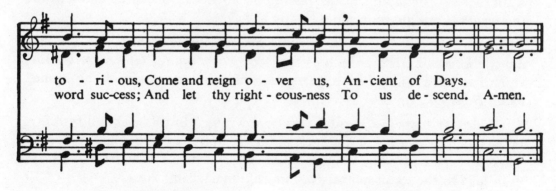

to-ri-ous, Come and reign o-ver us, An-cient of Days.
word suc-cess; And let thy right-eous-ness To us de-scend. A-men.

3 Come, Holy Comforter,
  Thy sacred witness bear
    In this glad hour:
  Thou who almighty art,
  Now rule in every heart,
  And ne'er from us depart,
    Spirit of power.

4 To thee, great One in Three,
  Eternal praises be,
    Hence, evermore!
  Thy sovereign majesty
  May we in glory see,
  And to eternity
    Love and adore. Amen.

WILLIAM WALFORD

1772 - June 22, 1850

William Walford was born in Bath, England, and educated at Homerton Academy. Ordained a Congregational minister in 1789, he served pastorates at Stowmarket, Suffolk and Great Yarmouth, Norfolk. Resigning from Great Yarmouth in 1813, Walford became classical tutor at Homerton Academy until 1824 when he accepted a call from the Old Meeting Congregational Church at Uxbridge (see photo on page 36). It was during Walford's pastorate that the Old Meeting Church made it's first structural alterations and got an organ (1828). It is not known which hymnal they used but because few people could read, it is recorded that a song leader read each verse before the congregation sang it. (A common practice in those days.) In 1831, plagued by ill health, Walford resigned to return to tutoring at Homerton Academy.

When in 1838, the Uxbridge Church again needed a pastor they asked Walford to return and his health having improved, he accepted and stayed nine years until his retirement in 1847.

Walford's published works include his own translation of the Psalms and the *Roman Letter* as well as the book *The Manner Of Prayer* (1836) which has been studied by experts to verify his authorship of the hymn *Sweet Hour Of Prayer!*

Of his last years in Uxbridge, Walford wrote, ''In this tranquil retreat, undisturbed by avarice or ambition or any tumultuous emotions, my latter years have passed with, I suppose, as large a measure of happiness as often falls to the lot of mortals in this sublunary condition.''

The biography of William Batchelder Bradbury, composer of the music to which we sing *Sweet Hour of Prayer!* is on page 136.

Sweet Hour Of Prayer

William W. Walford

William B. Bradbury

1. Sweet hour of prayer! sweet hour of prayer! That calls me from a world of care,
2. Sweet hour of prayer! sweet hour of prayer! The joys I feel, the bliss I share,
3. Sweet hour of prayer! sweet hour of prayer! Thy wings shall my pe - ti - tion bear

And bids me at my Fa-ther's throne Make all my wants and wish-es known;
Of those whose anx-ious spir - its burn With strong de-sires for thy re - turn!
To Him whose truth and faith-ful - ness En-gage the wait-ing soul to bless;

In sea-sons of dis-tress and grief, My soul has oft - en found re - lief;
With such I has - ten to the place Where God my Sav - iour shows His face,
And since He bids me seek His face, Be - lieve His Word and trust His grace,

And oft es-caped the tempt-er's snare, By thy re - turn, sweet hour of prayer
And glad - ly take my sta - tion there, And wait for thee, sweet hour of prayer!
I'll cast on Him my ev - ery care, And wait for thee, sweet hour of prayer! A-men.

SAMUEL JOHN STONE

April 25, 1839 - November 19, 1900

When in 1866 Bishop Colenso attacked the historical accuracy of the Pentateuch, Bishop Gray deposed Colenso, issuing a strong defense of church doctrine. As the controversy raged Samuel Stone, Curate of Windsor, wrote twelve hymns based on the Apostles' Creed, the ninth of which was *The Church's One Foundation.*

Samuel Stone was born in Whitmore, England, the son of an Anglican minister. He was educated at Charterhouse and at Pembroke College, Oxford. Ordained in the Church of England in 1862 he held pastorates at Windsor, St. Paul's and All-Hallows-On-The-Wall, London, where he remained until his death. During his life he published five collections of poems and hymns and a sixth was published posthumously.

SAMUEL SEBASTIAN WESLEY

August 14, 1810 - April 19, 1876

Samuel S. Wesley, composer of the music for *The Church's One Foundation* (and many others), was the son of Samuel Wesley and grandson of Charles Wesley.

Born in London, he attended Oxford University and became the greatest musical genius of the Wesley family and one of the most significant English church musicians of the 1800's.

It is said that only fishing could compete with his love of music and that he would accept or reject organist positions offered him according to the fishing advantages of the area.

During his great career, he served as organist for five parish churches, four major cathedrals and in 1850 became professor of organ at the Royal Academy of Music.

The Church's One Foundation

Samuel J. Stone   *Samuel S. Wesley*

1. The Church-'s one foun-da-tion Is Je-sus Christ her Lord;
2. E-lect from ev-ery na-tion, Yet one o'er all the earth,
3. 'Mid toil and trib-u-la-tion, And tu-mult of her war,
4. Yet she on earth hath un-ion With God the Three in One,

She is His new cre-a-tion By wa-ter and the word:
Her char-ter of sal-va-tion, One Lord, one faith, one birth;
She waits the con-sum-ma-tion Of peace for ev-er-more;
And mys-tic sweet com-mun-ion With those whose rest is won:

From heaven He came and sought her To be His ho-ly bride;
One ho-ly Name she bless-es, Par-takes one ho-ly food,
Till, with the vi-sion glo-rious, Her long-ing eyes are blest,
O hap-py ones and ho-ly! Lord, give us grace that we,

With His own blood He bought her, And for her life He died.
And to one hope she press-es, With ev-ery grace en-dued.
And the great Church vic-to-rious Shall be the Church at rest.
Like them, the meek and low-ly, On high may dwell with Thee. Amen.

ROBERT GRANT

1779 - July 9, 1838

Robert Grant, author of *O Worship The King*, was born in Bengal, India, the son of a director of the East India Company. When six years old they moved to London and Robert was educated at Magdalen College, Cambridge.

After college he became a prominent attorney. In 1818 he entered Parliament and in 1833 introduced a bill in Commons for removal of civil restrictions imposed upon Jews. In 1834 he was appointed Governor of Bombay and knighted. Four years later he died in Dalpoorie, India.

A very religious man, Robert Grant wrote twelve hymns which were published by his brother after his death under the title of *Sacred Poems* (1839).

JOHANN MICHAEL HAYDN

September 14, 1737 - August 10, 1806

Born in Rohrau, Austria, Johann was the younger brother of the famous composer Franz Joseph Haydn.

Like his older brother, Johann became a chorister at St. Stephen's, Vienna. In 1757, he went to Grosswardein as chapelmaster and in 1762, became musical director to Archbishop Sigismund of Salzburg, a position he maintained until his death at the age of sixty-nine.

During his career he wrote a number of oratorios - over one hundred instrumental works for organ and orchestras and more than four hundred sacred works, of which the music adapted for Grant's *O Worship The King* lives on even today, as a favorite of Christians everywhere.

O Worship The King

Robert Grant   *Adapted from Johann M. Haydn*

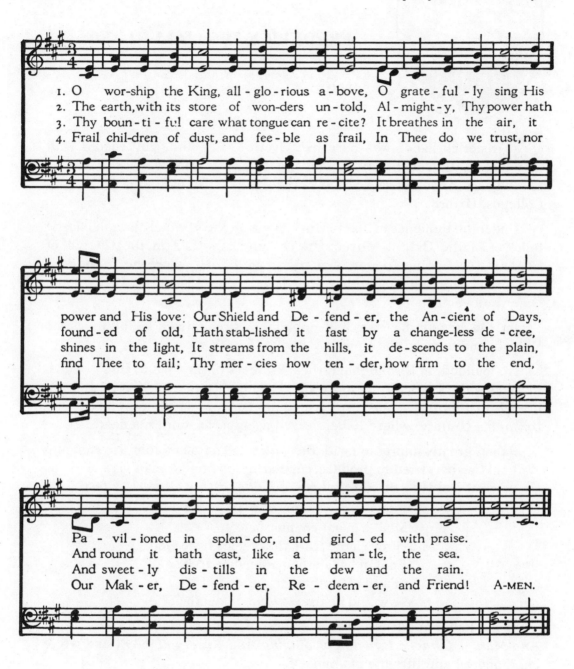

1. O wor-ship the King, all - glo-rious a-bove, O grate-ful-ly sing His
2. The earth, with its store of won-ders un-told, Al-might-y, Thy power hath
3. Thy boun-ti-ful care what tongue can re-cite? It breathes in the air, it
4. Frail chil-dren of dust, and fee-ble as frail, In Thee do we trust, nor

power and His love; Our Shield and De-fend-er, the An-cient of Days,
found-ed of old, Hath stab-lished it fast by a change-less de-cree,
shines in the light, It streams from the hills, it de-scends to the plain,
find Thee to fail; Thy mer-cies how ten-der, how firm to the end,

Pa - vil-ioned in splen-dor, and gird-ed with praise.
And round it hath cast, like a man-tle, the sea.
And sweet-ly dis-tills in the dew and the rain.
Our Mak-er, De-fend-er, Re-deem-er, and Friend! A-MEN.

FREDERICK WILLIAM FABER

June 28, 1814 - September 26, 1863

Frederick Faber was born in Calverley, England, and reared with strict Calvinistic discipline and teaching. He was educated at Shrewsbury and Harrow Schools and later at Balliol and University Colleges, Oxford.

Under the influence of John Henry Newman he became an enthusiastic follower of the Oxford Movement. Ordained in 1842 in the Church of England, he became rector of a parish in Elton, where he introduced penance, confession and other "Catholic" practices advocated by the Oxford Movement.

In 1846 he quit the Church of England was rebaptized taking the name Wilfrid and entered the Roman Catholic Church.

He founded, in Birmingham, the "Brothers of the Will of God" which merged with Newman's Oratory of St. Philip Neri in 1848. In 1849 a branch of this order was established in London which developed into *Brompton Oratory*, where Faber served as superior until his death.

Faber, greatly impressed with the *Olney* collection of John Newton and William Cowper, tried to produce popular hymns for Roman Catholics, as his original words to the third verse of *Faith Of Our Fathers*, attests:

"Faith of our Fathers! Mary's prayers
Shall win our country back to thee;
And through the truth that comes from God
England shall then indeed be free;
Faith of our Fathers! Holy faith!
We would be true to thee till death".

In all Faber published five collections of hymns, beginning with *Jesus And Mary -- Catholic Hymns For Singing And Reading* (1849), and wrote one hundred and fifty hymns himself.

The music to which we sing *Faith Of Our Fathers* was composed in 1864 by Henry Frederick Hemy, professor of music at St. Cuthbert's College, Ushaw, Durham, England and set to the Roman Catholic hymn, *St. Catherine, Virgin And Martyr*. Ten years later James George Walton added the final eight measures when he made this arrangement for his *Plain Song Music For The Holy Communion Office* (1874).

Faith Of Our Fathers!

Frederick W. Faber

Henry F. Hemy
Adapted by James G. Walton

1. Faith of our fa - thers! liv - ing still In spite of dun - geon, fire, and sword, O how our hearts beat high with joy When-e er we hear that glo - rious word! Faith of our fa - thers, ho - ly faith! We will be true to thee till death.

2. Faith of our fa - thers! we will strive To win all na - tions un - to thee, And through the truth that comes from God Man - kind shall then be tru - ly free. Faith of our fa - thers, ho - ly faith! We will be true to thee till death.

3. Faith of our fa - thers! we will love Both friend and foe in all our strife, And preach thee, too, as love knows how By kind - ly words and vir - tuous life: Faith of our fa - thers, ho - ly faith! We will be true to thee till death. A - MEN.

Silent Night In Stained Glass At St. Nicholas

When just before Christmas, in 1818, the organ at St. Nicholas Church, Oberndorf, Austria, broke, Father Joseph Mohr decided to write a hymn to be sung to guitar music. He wrote the words to *Silent Night* and asked the organist, Franz Gruber, to compose music for two voices and a guitar. That Christmas eve, the organ stilled, guitar music filled St. Nicholas Church as *Silent Night* was sung for the first time. Copies of the song were circulated but it did not become widely known until it was sung at the Leipzig Fair in 1831. A Dresden musician named Friese was in the audience; he copied it down, took it to Berlin and from there it became famous worldwide.

JOSEPH MOHR

December 11, 1792 - December 4, 1848

Born in Salzburg, Austria, Joseph was a chorister in the Salzburg church as a boy. In 1815 he was ordained a priest in the Roman Catholic Church and from August 1817 to October 19, 1819, served as assistant priest at St. Nicholas Church, Oberndorf, Austria. It was during this time that he wrote the words to *Silent Night*. Father Mohr went on to several other appointments, his last being vicar at Wagrein in 1837.

Silent Night

Joseph Mohr

Franz Gruber

1. Si - lent night, ho - ly night, All is calm, all is bright;
2. Si - lent night, ho - ly night, Dark - ness flies, all is light;
3. Si - lent night, ho - ly night, Son of God, love's pure light;
4. Si - lent night, ho - ly night, Won - drous Star, lend thy light;

Round yon Vir - gin Moth - er and Child! Ho - ly In-fant, so ten-der and mild,
Shep - herds hear the an - gels sing, "Al - le - lu - ia! hail the King!
Ra - diant beams from Thy ho - ly face, With the dawn of re - deem-ing grace,
With the an - gels let us sing, Al - le - lu - ia to our King;

Sleep in heav - en - ly peace, Sleep in heav - en - ly peace.
Christ the Sav - iour is born, Christ the Sav - iour is born."
Je - sus, Lord, at Thy birth, Je - sus, Lord, at Thy birth.
Christ the Sav - iour is born, Christ the Sav - iour is born.

A - MEN.

FRANZ XAVER GRUBER

November 25, 1787 - June 7, 1863

Franz was born in Unterweizberg, Austria, the son of a poor linen weaver. Loving music, Franz, without his father's knowledge, learned to play the violin and later studied organ. From 1807 to 1829 he was a school teacher and to supplement his income was organist at nearby St. Nicholas. Franz Gruber wrote more than ninety compositions during his career. He became headmaster at Berndorf and from 1833 until his death, organist and choirmaster at Hallein, near Salzburg.

ROBERT ROBINSON

September 27, 1735 - June 9, 1790

Robert Robinson was born in Swaffham, England. His father died when he was a child and at the age of fourteen he was sent off to London, apprenticed to a barber.

When Robert was seventeen a sermon by George Whitefield lead him, at age twenty, to make a confession of faith. He began to preach and became pastor of a Calvinistic Methodist Chapel in Mindenhall. Later he organized an independent congregation at Norwich. In 1761, he again changed affiliations and for the next twenty-nine years served as pastor of the Stone Yard Baptist Church in Cambridge, England. Although lacking formal education Robert rose to great prominence, writing many theological works and in 1790, a *History Of The Baptists*.

JOHN WYETH

March 31, 1770 - January 23, 1858

John Wyeth wrote the music to which we sing *Come Thou Fount Of Every Blessing*. In 1810 he published *Repository Of Sacred Music*, which sold one hundred and fifty thousand copies.

Born in Cambridge, Massachusetts, Wyeth was apprenticed out to a printer as a young boy. When twenty-one years old he became superintendent of a large printing firm in Santo Domingo only to lose everything, and narrowly escaping death, in The Black Insurrection. He returned to the Colonies, settling at Harrisburg, Pennsylvania in 1792. Here he became co-owner of *The Oracle Of Dauphin* newspaper, a bookstore and book publishing company.

President George Washington appointed him postmaster of Harrisburg in 1793 but in 1798 President John Adams removed him from office citing, "the incompatibility of the office of postmaster and editor of a newspaper".

Come, Thou Fount

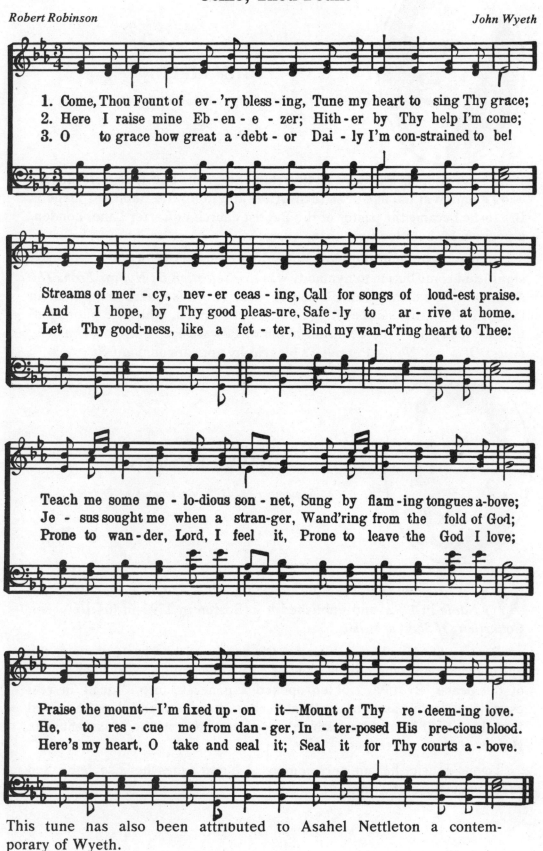

Robert Robinson   *John Wyeth*

1. Come, Thou Fount of ev-'ry bless-ing, Tune my heart to sing Thy grace;
2. Here I raise mine Eb-en-e-zer; Hith-er by Thy help I'm come;
3. O   to grace how great a debt-or Dai-ly I'm con-strained to be!

Streams of mer-cy, nev-er ceas-ing, Call for songs of loud-est praise.
And   I hope, by Thy good pleas-ure, Safe-ly to ar-rive at home.
Let   Thy good-ness, like a fet-ter, Bind my wan-d'ring heart to Thee:

Teach me some me-lo-dious son-net, Sung by flam-ing tongues a-bove;
Je-sus sought me when a stran-ger, Wand'ring from the fold of God;
Prone to wan-der, Lord, I feel it, Prone to leave the God I love;

Praise the mount—I'm fixed up-on it—Mount of Thy re-deem-ing love.
He, to res-cue me from dan-ger, In-ter-posed His pre-cious blood.
Here's my heart, O take and seal it; Seal it for Thy courts a-bove.

This tune has also been attributed to Asahel Nettleton a contemporary of Wyeth.

67

JOHN RIPPON

April 29, 1751 - December 17, 1836

John Rippon was born in Riverton, England, and joined its Baptist church at the age of sixteen. After attending the Baptist College in Bristol he became the pastor of the Baptist church at Carter Lane, London, a position he held for sixty-three years.

Rippon was one of the most influential ministers of his day. His most significant contribution to hymnody was his *Selection Of Hymns From The Best Authors* which became a source book for subsequent compilers. In fact, it is from this source (Rippon's altered version, which he published) that we today have the beautiful hymn of Edward Perronet *All Hail The Power Of Jesus' Name.* Perronet's biography appears on page 70.

OLIVER HOLDEN

September 18, 1765 - September 4, 1844

Oliver Holden composed the music for *All Hail The Power Of Jesus' Name* in 1792 and published it in Boston in 1793 in his *Universal Collection Of Sacred Music.*

Born in Shirley, Massachusetts, Oliver moved to Charlestown at the age of twenty-one where he worked as carpenter and also served as justice of the peace. By 1790 Holden opened a general store, "dealt in real estate", and was pastor of the local Puritan church. In addition, he served from 1818 to 1833 as Charlestown's representative in the Massachusetts House of Representatives.

Loving music, he not only composed hymn tunes he also published seven collections of hymns.

All Hail The Power Of Jesus' Name

Edward Perronet
Alt. by John Rippon

Oliver Holden

1. All hail the power of Je-sus' Name! Let an-gels pros-trate fall;
2. Ye cho-sen seed of Is-rael's race, Ye ran-somed from the fall,
3. Sin-ners, whose love can ne'er for-get The worm-wood and the gall,

Bring forth the roy-al di-a-dem, And crown Him Lord of all;
Hail Him who saves you by His grace, And crown Him Lord of all;
Go, spread your tro-phies at His feet, And crown Him Lord of all;

Bring forth the roy-al di-a-dem, And crown Him Lord of all.
Hail Him who saves you by His grace, And crown Him Lord of all.
Go, spread your tro-phies at His feet, And crown Him Lord of all. A-MEN.

4 Let every kindred, every tribe,
   On this terrestrial ball,
   To Him all majesty ascribe,
   And crown Him Lord of all.

5 O that with yonder sacred throng
   We at His feet may fall!
   We'll join the everlasting song,
   And crown Him Lord of all.

EDWARD PERRONET

1726 - January 2, 1792

Edward Perronet, author of *All Hail The Power Of Jesus' Name* (page 75) was born in Sundridge, England, to a family of Huguenot refugees. His father became prominently known as Vicar of Shoreham and Edward became a close friend and co-worker of John and Charles Wesley. In 1757 Edward wrote a poem, *The Mitre*, attacking the Church of England so viciously that it angered the Wesleys. Perronet left, spending his last years as pastor of a small independent chapel at Canterbury.

JOHANN [HANS] GEORG NÄGELI

May 26, 1773 - December 26, 1836

Born in Wetzikon, Switzerland, little is known of Johann's early life. In 1792 he established a music publishing company and founded the Swiss Association for the Cultivation of Music. In 1826 he published the first music "Appreciation" textbook to cultivate the ability to listen to seriously conceived music.

Johann Nägeli was a pioneer in music education. He taught the principle of the Pestalozzian system and through it influenced the great American composer and music teacher, Lowell Mason.

JOHN FAWCETT

January 6, 1740 - July 25, 1817

John Fawcett, born in Lidget Green, England, was another young convert of George Whitefield. He became associated with the Methodists and attended the Church of England. When eighteen years old he joined the Baptist church at Bradford. At the age of twenty-three he was ordained and became the pastor of the Baptist church at Wainsgate, in the hills above Hebden Bridge. (Continued under hymn on page 71.)

Blest Be The Tie That Binds

John Fawcett   *Johann Nageli*

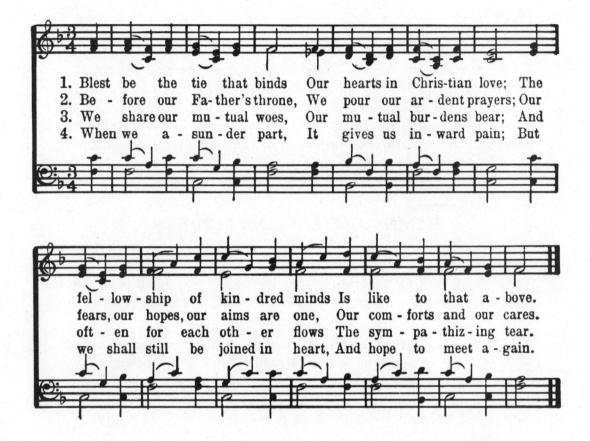

1. Blest be the tie that binds Our hearts in Chris-tian love; The
2. Be - fore our Fa-ther's throne, We pour our ar - dent prayers; Our
3. We share our mu - tual woes, Our mu - tual bur-dens bear; And
4. When we a - sun-der part, It gives us in - ward pain; But

fel - low-ship of kin - dred minds Is like to that a - bove.
fears, our hopes, our aims are one, Our com - forts and our cares.
oft - en for each oth - er flows The sym - pa - thiz-ing tear.
we shall still be joined in heart, And hope to meet a - gain.

(John Fawcett's biography continued.)

In 1772, the Carter Lane Baptist Chapel in London offered John Faucett 40 pounds a year to come to their church succeeding the famous Dr. J. Gill. Fawcett told his congregation that unless they raised his salary he would have to accept. When the congregation said they couldn't afford 40 pounds he sold some of his furniture preparing to move; then at their pleading, he changed his mind. Deciding to stay, he wrote *Blest Be The Tie That Binds,* celebrating the reason for which he could not leave.

By 1777 the population had moved to Hebden Bridge, so Fawcett with fifty church members erected Ebenezer Church (now Hope Baptist) at Hebden Bridge.

John Fawcett founded at Ebenezer Baptist, the Northern Education Society, which is today the Rawdon College. During his ministry Fawcett wrote a great number of hymns which he used at the conclusion of his sermons.

FOLLIOTT SANFORD PIERPOINT

October 7, 1835 - March 10, 1917

Folliott Pierpoint was born at Bath, England, and was educated at Queen's College, Cambridge, graduating in 1857.

For several years he was classical master at Somersetshire College. After resigning he lived at Babbicombe and other places doing occasional teaching. He published several volumes of poetry and wrote a number of hymns, including *For The Beauty Of The Earth* which William Henry Monk selected for *Hymns Ancient And Modern* and arranged the music.

HYMNS ANCIENT AND MODERN

Forces at work for several decades paved the way for this significant compilation. The new concepts of worship being promoted by the Oxford Movement called for new hymns.

In September of 1858 an initial meeting was held in London to discuss the publishing of a new type of hymnal, which came to be known as *Hymns Ancient And Modern.* In October advertisements were placed soliciting contributions for the proposed hymnal and more than two hundred suggestions were received by Henry William Baker, secretary of the Committee.

In this new hymnal of high church spirit, provisions were made for appropriate hymns for days of the week, feasts, fasts, services of the *Book Of Common Prayer,* occasions and saints days, including the Annunciation and Purification of the Beloved Virgin Mary.

Of its two hundred and seventy-three hymns, one hundred and thirty-one were of English origin (twelve being new hymns), one hundred thirty-two were Latin translations and ten were German translations.

The first music edition, with William H. Monk as music editor, was published in 1861. Monk and his assistants carefully avoided tunes of evangelical origin of the 1700's. Of their new tunes Monk contributed seventeen, John B. Dykes, seven and Frederick A.G. Ouseley, five.

Hymns Ancient And Modern became a national institution, selling over one hundred and fifty million copies and its imprint is still evident. All subsequent compilers have reprinted its liturgical hymns, copied its format and maintained many of the marriages of texts and tunes which appeared there, together, for the first time.

For The Beauty Of The Earth

Folliott S. Pierpoint

Abridged by W.H. Monk from a chorale by
Conrad Kocher, 1786-1872

1. For the beau-ty of the earth, For the glo-ry of the skies,
2. For the beau-ty of each hour Of the day and of the night,
3. For the joy of ear and eye; For the heart and mind's de-light;
4. For the joy of hu-man love, Broth-er, sis-ter, par-ent, child,

For the love which from our birth O-ver and a-round us lies:
Hill and vale, and tree and flower, Sun and moon, and stars of light:
For the mys-tic har-mo-ny Link-ing sense to sound and sight:
Friends on earth, and friends a-bove; For all gen-tle thoughts and mild:

Lord of all, to Thee we raise This our hymn of grate-ful praise. A-MEN.

5 For Thy church, that evermore
  Lifteth holy hands above,
Offering up on every shore
  Her pure sacrifice of love:
Lord of all, to Thee we raise
This our hymn of grateful praise.

6 For Thyself, best Gift Divine!
  To our race so freely given;
For that great, great love of Thine,
  Peace on earth, and joy in heaven:
Lord of all, to Thee we raise
This our hymn of grateful praise.

HENRY FRANCIS LYTE

June 1, 1793 - November 20, 1847

Henry Francis Lyte was born in Ednam, Scotland, and educated in Dublin, Ireland. He was ordained in 1815. After serving several churches he was appointed curate at the beautiful All Saints' Church, Brixham, Devonshire in 1824. Here, Lyte ministered to the people of this fishing village for twenty-three years, increased church membership from five hundred to fifteen hundred, developed a Sunday school and wrote many beautiful hymns as well as rewriting all one hundred and fifty psalms, in the form of hymns. A frail man, he suffered from asthma and consumption. He was like a father to the fishermen. No ship left the harbor until Vicar Lyte had blessed it. He retired and while enroute to Sicily for a vacation, died in Nice, France, just four months after having written his most loved hymn, *Abide With Me*, at his beloved waterfront home in Brixham.

WILLIAM HENRY MONK

March 16, 1823 - March 1, 1889

William Henry Monk lived all of his life in London. He served as organist at various London churches and the King's College until 1852 when he became organist at St. Matthias Church, Stoke Newington, a position he held until his death.

Of extraordinary significance was the role he played in writing music, and adapting music and lyrics, when music editor for England's most popular hymnal *Hymns Ancient And Modern*.

74

Abide With Me

Henry F. Lyte   *William H. Monk*

1. A - bide with me: fast falls the e - ven - tide; The dark - ness
2. Swift to its close ebbs out life's lit - tle day; Earth's joys grow
3. I need Thy pres - ence ev - ery pass - ing hour; What but Thy

deep - ens; Lord, with me a - bide! When oth - er help - ers
dim, its glo - ries pass a - way; Change and de - cay in
grace can foil the tempt - er's power? Who, like Thy - self, my

fail, and com - forts flee, Help of the help - less, O a - bide with me.
all a - round I see; O Thou, who chang - est not, a - bide with me.
guide and stay can be? Thro' cloud and sun - shine, Lord, a - bide with me. A - MEN.

4 I fear no foe, with Thee at hand to bless;
Ills have no weight, and tears no bitterness.
Where is death's sting? where, grave, thy victory?
I triumph still, if Thou abide with me.

5 Hold Thou Thy cross before my closing eyes;
Shine through the gloom and point me to the skies;
Heaven's morning breaks, and earth's vain shadows flee;
In life, in death, O Lord, abide with me.

HENRY WILLIAMS BAKER

May 27, 1821 -February 12, 1877

enry Baker was born in London, educated at Trinity College, Cambridge and ordained in the Church of England in 1844. He became Vicar of Monkland, Hertfordshire and remained there until his death. Baker was the man largely responsible for England's most famous hymnal, *Hymns Ancient And Modern,* and was knighted in 1859 in recognition of his service as Chairman of the Editorial Committee for almost twenty years.

JOHN BACCHUS DYKES

March 10, 1823 - January 22, 1876

ohn Bacchus Dykes, born in Hull, England, was the son of a banker and grandson of a minister. A musical prodigy, he played the organ in his grandfather's church at the age of ten. After graduation from St. Catharine's College, Cambridge in 1847 he was ordained a priest in the Church of England in 1848 and served various parishes. In 1861 Dykes earned his doctorate and in 1862 became Vicar of St. Oswald's, Durham, where he served until his death, (which some say was caused by a bitter feud between Dykes and his bishop.)

The feud began when Dykes asked for a curate to assist him and his bishop replied that he would give help only if Dykes would promise: 1) never to wear colored stoles; 2) never to use incense; and 3) never to stand with his back to the congregation. Dykes refused saying, "No other priest had ever been subject to such humiliation". The Court of the Queen's Bench ruled that the bishop had jurisdiction. Two years later John Dykes died.

A prolific composer and great musician, John Dykes wrote about three hundred compositions including our most loved hymns, *Holy, Holy, Holy!; The King Of Love My Shepherd Is* and *Jesus, Lover Of My Soul.*

The King of Love My Shepherd Is

From Psalm 23
Henry W. Baker

John B. Dykes

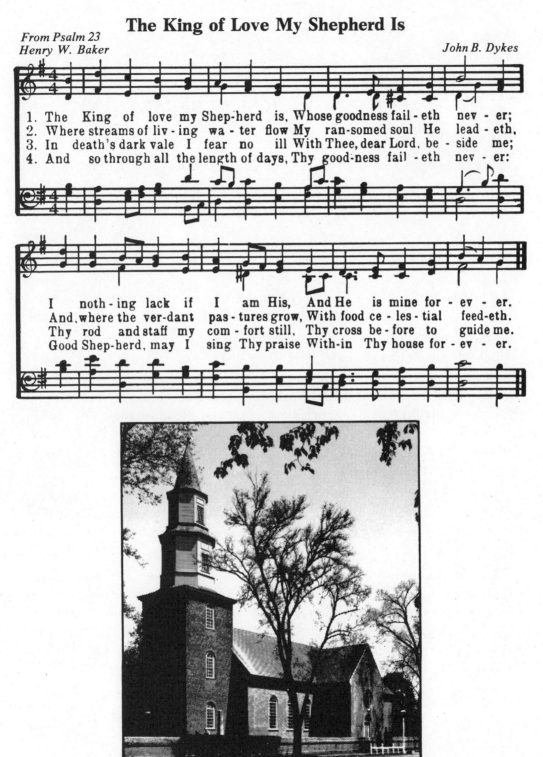

1. The King of love my Shep-herd is, Whose goodness fail-eth nev-er;
2. Where streams of liv-ing wa-ter flow My ran-somed soul He lead-eth,
3. In death's dark vale I fear no ill With Thee, dear Lord, be-side me;
4. And so through all the length of days, Thy good-ness fail-eth nev-er:

I noth-ing lack if I am His, And He is mine for-ev-er.
And, where the ver-dant pas-tures grow, With food ce-les-tial feed-eth.
Thy rod and staff my com-fort still, Thy cross be-fore to guide me.
Good Shep-herd, may I sing Thy praise With-in Thy house for-ev-er.

Bruton Parish Episcopal Church, Williamsburg

George Washington, Thomas Jefferson, Patrick Henry and other notable leaders of Virginia attended Bruton Parish Church when Williamsburg was the capital of Virginia. Originating in 1633, the present church was chartered and built in 1715 by the Church of England and today serves a congregation of over five hundred members.

JOSEPH BARNBY

August 12, 1838 - January 28, 1896

The beautiful hymn *When Morning Gilds The Skies* was an obscure writing by an anonymous German author, until joined with the music of Joseph Barnby in *Hymns Ancient And Modern.*

Joseph Barnby was born in York, England. A musical prodigy, he was a chorister at York Minster at the age of seven, played organ at his church at the age of twelve and was York Minster choirmaster at the age of fourteen. After receiving his formal music education at the Royal Academy of Music, he was organist for several churches, St. Michael's, St. James the Less, St. Andrew's and for St. Anne's in Soho, which was known for its annual presentation of Passion music.

From 1875 to 1896, Barnby was precentor and musical advisor to Eaton College and to Novello and Company. Barnby also served as principal of the Guildhall School of Music and conducted various annual music festivals.

Barnby was editor of four collections of music and assisted in the preparation of *The Cathedral Psalter* of 1873. His compositions include the oratorio *Rebekah, Psalm 97,* forty-five anthems and organ and piano pieces, as well as two hundred forty-six hymn tunes, all of which were published in one volume after his death. In recognition of Joseph Barnby's great contribution to music he was knighted in 1892.

When Morning Gilds The Skies

tr. Edward Caswall [1854]

Joseph Barnby

1. When morn-ing gilds the skies, My heart a-wak-ing cries,
2. When-e'er the sweet church bell Peals o-ver hill and dell,
3. The night be-comes as day, When from the heart we say,
4. Ye na-tions of man-kind, In this your con-cord find,

May Je-sus Christ be praised! A-like at work and prayer,
May Je-sus Christ be praised! O hark to what it sings,
May Je-sus Christ be praised! The powers of dark-ness fear,
May Je-sus Christ be praised! Let all the earth a-round

To Je-sus I re-pair; May Je-sus Christ be praised!
As joy-ous-ly it rings, May Je-sus Christ be praised!
When this sweet chant they hear, May Je-sus Christ be praised!
Ring joy-ous with the sound, May Je-sus Christ be praised! A-MEN.

5 In heaven's eternal bliss
The loveliest strain is this,
  May Jesus Christ be praised!
Let earth, and sea, and sky
From depth to height reply,
  May Jesus Christ be praised!

6 Be this, while life is mine,
My canticle divine,
  May Jesus Christ be praised!
Be this th' eternal song
Through all the ages long,
  May Jesus Christ be praised!

SABINE BARING-GOULD

January 28, 1834 - January 2, 1924

Sabine Baring-Gould wrote *Onward, Christian Soldiers* in 1864 for a children's festival, "procession with cross and banners", at Horbury Bridge, Yorkshire, England.

Sabine Baring-Gould was born in Exeter, England, the son of an English squire, He spent much of his early life in Germany and France. Educated at Clare College, Cambridge, he was ordained a priest in the Church of England in 1864. He became Curate of Horbury, with charge of the children's mission at Horbury Bridge, for whom he wrote his best known hymns.

In 1881, having inherited the family estate, he became rector of Lew-Trenchard. During his career, Sabine Baring-Gould wrote books on history, biography, poetry, and fiction, in addition to his hymns and his famous collection of folk songs.

ARTHUR SEYMOUR SULLIVAN

May 13, 1842 - November 22, 1900

The music to *Onward, Christian Soldiers* was written by that musical genius known to most people by his company name, Gilbert and Sullivan.

Born in Bolwell Terrace, England, he was a chorister at the Royal Chapel at the age of twelve. He was educated at the Royal Academy of Music and the Leipzig Conservatory. After his return to England he held several organist positions. In 1866 he became professor of composition at the Royal Academy of Music and wrote most of his hymn tunes during this period (1867-1874).

When Sullivan became associated with Sir W. S. Gilbert, they composed operettas for the Savoy Operas, and soon, all the world came to know of Gilbert and Sullivan.

Onward Christian Soldiers

Sabine Baring-Gould

Arthur S. Sullivan

1. On - ward, Chris-tian sol - diers! March-ing as to war, With the cross of
2. Like a might - y arm - y Moves the Church of God; Broth-ers, we are
3. Crowns and thrones may per - ish, King-doms rise and wane, But the Church of
4. On - ward, then, ye peo - ple, Join our hap - py throng, Blend with ours your

Je - sus Go - ing on be - fore. Christ, the roy - al Mas - ter,
tread-ing Where the saints have trod; We are not di - vid - ed,
Je - sus Con - stant will re - main; Gates of hell can nev - er
voic - es In the tri - umph-song; Glo - ry, laud, and hon - or

Leads a - gainst the foe; For-ward in - to bat - tle, See His ban -ners go!
All one bod - y we, One in hope and doc - trine, One in char - i - ty.
Gainst that Church pre-vail; We have Christ's own prom-ise, And that can - not fail.
Un - to Christ the King; This thro' count-less a - ges Men and an - gels sing.

REFRAIN

On - ward, Chris - tian sol - diers, March-ing as to war,

With the cross of Je - sus Go - ing on be - fore. A-MEN.

HENRY THOMAS SMART

October 26, 1813 - July 6, 1879

Henry Smart, composer of the music to which we sing *Lead On, O King Eternal,* was born in London. He studied law at Highgate but abandoned it in favor of music. Although mostly self-taught, he became one of the finest organists of his day. Between 1831 and when he died in 1879, he served as organist at Blackburn, Lancashire, St. Philip's Church, St. Luke's Church, and St. Pancras Church, London.

He wrote a great deal of church music and in addition to publishing two collections of his own, served as music editor for *Psalms And Hymns For Divine Worship* (1867) and the *Presbyterian Hymnal* (1875), the hymnbook of the United Presbyterian Church of Scotland.

In 1865 Smart, who had always had poor eyesight, became totally blind, but his skill was so great that he continued as organist of St. Pancras until his death in 1879.

ERNEST WARBURTON SHURTLEFF

April 4, 1862 - August 24, 1917

Ernest W. Shurtleff wrote *Lead On, O King Eternal,* setting it to a composition by Henry Smart for his graduation class from Andover Theological Seminary in 1887 and published it that year in his *Hymns Of Faith.*

Born in Boston, Ernest was educated at the Boston Latin School, Harvard University, New Church Theological Seminary and Andover Theological Seminary. Ordained a Congregational minister, he held pastorates at Ventura, California, Old Plymouth and Palmer, Massachusetts and the First Congregational Church of Minneapolis. In 1905 he organized the American Church at Frankfurt, Germany and in 1906 became director of student activities at the Academy Vitti.

Lead On, O King Eternal

Ernest W. Shurtleff

Henry Smart

1. Lead on, O King E - ter - nal, The day of march has come;
2. Lead on, O King E - ter - nal, Till sin's fierce war shall cease,
3. Lead on, O King E - ter - nal: We fol - low, not with fears,

Hence-forth in fields of con - quest Thy tents shall be our home:
And Ho - li - ness shall whis - per The sweet A - men of peace;
For glad-ness breaks like morn - ing Wher-e'er Thy face ap - pears;

Thro' days of prep - a - ra - tion Thy grace has made us strong,
For not with swords loud clash - ing, Nor roll of stir - ring drums;
Thy cross is lift - ed o'er us; We jour - ney in its light:

And now, O King E - ter - nal, We lift our bat - tle song.
With deeds of love and mer - cy, The heav'n-ly king-dom comes.
The crown a - waits the con - quest; Lead on, O God of might. A-MEN.

FRANCES RIDLEY HAVERGAL

December 14, 1836 - June 3, 1879

Frances Havergal was born in Astley, England, the youngest child of Reverend William H. Havergal, Vicar of Astley, Worcestershire. At the age of seven, she wrote poems which were published in several religious periodicals. Although her health was very frail she was an excellent student, mastering French, German, Italian, Greek and Hebrew. Her father, Reverend Havergal, himself a hymn writer and composer wrote the music to which *Take My Life, And Let It Be* is frequently sung in England and used to affectionately call her "Little Quicksilver".

Frances became one of the most talented and popular hymn writers of her day. When at the age of forty-two she was informed she was going to die soon, she replied "If I am going to, it is too good to be true". She died while reciting *Jesus I Will Trust Thee*. Her epitaph, as she requested, reads "The blood of Jesus Christ, His Son, cleanseth us from all sin".

When Frances Havergal wrote *Take My Life, And Let It Be* in 1874, the third verse "Take my silver and my gold, not a mite would I withhold", was not just poetry, for in August of 1874, Frances wrote to a friend:

"The Lord has shown me another little step, and of course I have taken it with extreme delight. 'Take my silver and my gold', now means shipping off all my ornaments to the Church Missionary House (including a jewel cabinet that is really fit for a countess), where all will be accepted and disposed of for me. I retain a brooch or two for daily wear, which are memorials of my dear parents, also a locket containing a portrait of my dear niece in heaven, my Evelyn, and her two rings; but these I redeem, so that the whole value goes to the Church Missionary Society. Nearly fifty articles are being packed up. I don't think I ever packed a box with such pleasure."

Take My Life, and Let It Be

Frances R. Havergal

H.A. Cesar Malan

1. Take my life, and let it be Con-se-crat-ed, Lord, to Thee; Take my hands, and
2. Take my feet, and let them be Swift and beau-ti-ful for Thee; Take my voice, and
3. Take my lips, and let them be Filled with messages for Thee; Take my sil - ver
4. Take my love, my God, I pour At Thy feet its treas-ure store; Take my-self and

let them move At the im-pulse of Thy love, At the im-pulse of Thy love.
let me sing Al-ways, on - ly, for my King, Al-ways, on - ly, for my King.
and my gold, Not a mite would I with-hold, Not a mite would I with-hold.
I will be Ev - er, on - ly, all for Thee, Ev - er, on - ly, all for Thee.

HENRI ABRAHAM CESAR MALAN

July 7, 1787 - May 18, 1864

Henri Malan was born in Geneva, Switzerland, and received his M.A. from the College of Geneva. After he was ordained in 1810 he became a popular preacher and founded a chapel in his own garden, preaching there for the next forty-three years.

Malan, who has been called by some the "greatest name in French hymnody", wrote more than one thousand hymns setting them to his own tunes, but only one tune, that used for *Take My Life, And Let It Be* remains popular.

JAMES RUSSELL LOWELL

February 22, 1819 - August 12, 1891

James Russell Lowell was born in Cambridge, Massachusetts, a descendant of Perceval Lowle, who immigrated to Massachusetts in 1639 founding one of the most famous New England families. His father was pastor of the West Congregational Church in Boston for fifty-five years.

Russell graduated from Harvard in 1838 and vacillated between business, medicine, the ministry and law, finally selecting law for his career.

An ardent champion of Abolition, his writing of *The Bigelow Papers* brought him sudden fame. In 1876 President Hayes appointed him minister to the court of Spain and in 1880 he was transferred to the court of St. James as minister to Great Britain. His reputation, as a man of letters, preceded him to England and he was in great demand as a public speaker whose words were widely quoted.

His great hymn, *Once To Every Man And Nation,* is an adaptation from his poem, *The Present Crisis.*

James Russell Lowell was a member of the Unitarian Church, as were three other authors of our 101 famous hymns, Julia Ward Howe, Sarah Flower Adams and Henry Wadsworth Longfellow.

THOMAS JOHN WILLIAMS

1869 - 1944

Little is known of Thomas Williams, composer of the music to which we sing *Once To Every Man And Nation,* except that he was born in Ynysmeudwy, Wales. After studying under David Evans he became the organist and choirmaster of Zion Church in Llanelly, Wales. In 1913 he moved to Calfaria Church (also in Llanelly) and remained there for over thirty years as choirmaster and organist.

Once To Every Man and Nation

James Russell Lowell   *Thomas John Williams*

1. Once to ev-ery man and na-tion Comes the mo-ment to de-cide,
   In the strife of truth with false-hood, For the good or e-vil side;
   Some great cause, God's new mes-si-ah, Of-fering each the bloom or blight,
   And the choice goes by for ev-er 'Twixt that dark-ness and that light.

2. Then to side with truth is no-ble, When we share her wretch-ed crust,
   Ere her cause bring fame and prof-it, And 'tis pros-perous to be just;
   Then it is the brave man choos-es, While the cow-ard stands a-side,
   Till the mul-ti-tude make vir-tue Of the faith they had de-nied.

3 By the light of burning martyrs,
   Christ, thy bleeding feet we track,
  Toiling up new Calvaries ever
   With the Cross that turns not back.
  New occasions teach new duties;
   Time makes ancient good uncouth;
  They must upward still and onward
   Who would keep abreast of truth.

4 Though the cause of evil prosper,
   Yet 'tis truth alone is strong;
  Though her portion be the scaffold
   And upon the throne be wrong,
  Yet that scaffold sways the future,
   And, behind the dim unknown,
  Standeth God within the shadow,
   Keeping watch above his own.

87

JOHN BAPTISTE CALKIN

March 16, 1827 - April 15, 1905

orn in London, John Calkin composer of the music for *I Heard The Bells On Christmas Day*, learned music from his father, a well known music teacher. At the age of twenty he succeeded E.G. Monk as organist at St. Columba's College near Dublin, Ireland. Returning to London, in 1853, he held various organist positions. In 1883 he was appointed to the faculty of the Guildhall School of Music.

HENRY WADSWORTH LONGFELLOW

February 27, 1807 - March 24, 1882

ongfellow was born in Portland, Maine, to a distinguished New England family. His mother, Zilpah, was a descendant of John Alden and Priscilla Mullins. Upon graduation from Bowdoin College at the age of eighteen he went to Europe to study. Upon his return he served as professor of literature and modern languages at Bowdoin College from 1829 to 1834. Late in 1834, he became professor of literature at Harvard University and remained there for seventeen years.

In 1861 Longfellow's wife tragically died when her dress caught fire in their beautiful Cambridge home. His writing, *The Children's Hour*, gives us an idea of the beauty of his home life, with his two sons and three daughters.

Among Longfellow's literary works are the immortal poems, *Evangeline* (1847), *The Song Of Hiawatha* (1855), *The Courtship Of Miles Standish* (1858) and *Tales Of A Wayside Inn* (1863).

Henry Wadsworth Longfellow was honored with the degree of LL.D.,

(Continued on next page.)

I Heard the Bells On Christmas Day

Henry W. Longfellow

J. Baptiste Calkin

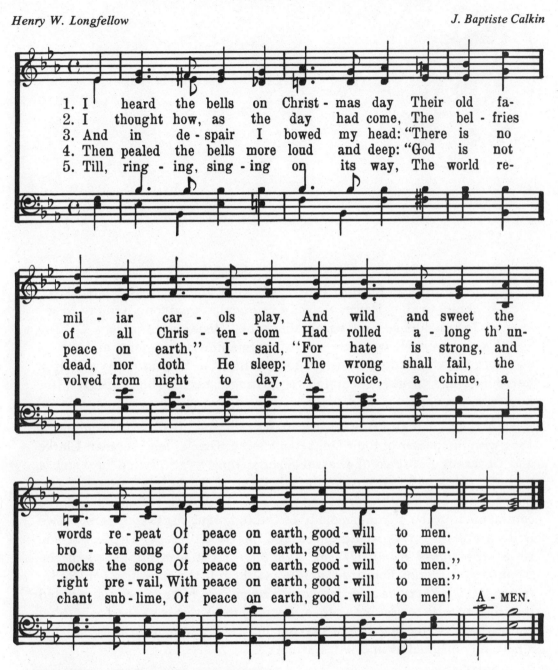

1. I heard the bells on Christ - mas day Their old fa -
2. I thought how, as the day had come, The bel - fries
3. And in de - spair I bowed my head: "There is no
4. Then pealed the bells more loud and deep: "God is not
5. Till, ring - ing, sing - ing on its way, The world re -

mil - iar car - ols play, And wild and sweet the
of all Chris - ten - dom Had rolled a - long th' un -
peace on earth," I said, "For hate is strong, and
dead, nor doth He sleep; The wrong shall fail, the
volved from night to day, A voice, a chime, a

words re - peat Of peace on earth, good - will to men.
bro - ken song Of peace on earth, good - will to men.
mocks the song Of peace on earth, good - will to men."
right pre - vail, With peace on earth, good - will to men:"
chant sub - lime, Of peace on earth, good - will to men! A - MEN.

(Longfellow's biography continued.)

by Harvard University and Cambridge (England) and in 1869, an D.C.L. degree from Oxford University. After his death in 1882, a bust was placed to his memory in the Poet's Corner in Westminster Abbey.

I Heard The Bells On Christmas Day was written by Henry Wadsworth Longfellow in 1864 for the Sunday school of the Unitarian Church of the Disciples in Boston and entitled, *Christmas Bells.*

JULIA WARD HOWE

May 27, 1819 - October 17, 1910

Julia Ward was born in New York City, and in 1848 married Dr. Samuel Gridley Howe, who as a young man had fought in the Greek War of Independence and wrote the book, *Historical Sketches Of The Greek Revolution*. He was very active in humanitarian interests and served as director of the Perkins Institute for the Blind in Boston. Julia joined in her husband's work, becoming a distinguished public speaker for humanitarian causes.

When she and Dr. Howe were in Washington, D.C. in December of 1861 with the pastor of their Unitarian church, Dr. James Freeman Clarke and Governor Andrews of Massachusetts, they were invited to watch a military review of federal troops outside the city. On their return to the city, the road was congested with troops singing *John Brown's Body*. Dr. Clarke commented on the stirring melody of the tune and suggested Mrs. Howe write words for it that would encourage the Union forces. That night she wrote *The Battle Hymn Of The Republic* and it was published in the *Atlantic Monthly* in February of 1862. Although the tune for *The Battle Hymn Of The Republic* and also *John Brown's Body* have been attributed to William Steffe, no one can prove why they think this is so. The only thing known for sure is that it is a variant of an old camp meeting tune that apparently originated in South Carolina.

Julia Howe continued her writing and speaking career and at one point, proposed that the women of the world unite to end war for all time. She was a very active writer and speaker all her life, writing three volumes of verse and preaching in Unitarian churches and those of other denominations, as well as giving public lectures.

Battle Hymn of the Republic

Julia Ward Howe

Anonymous

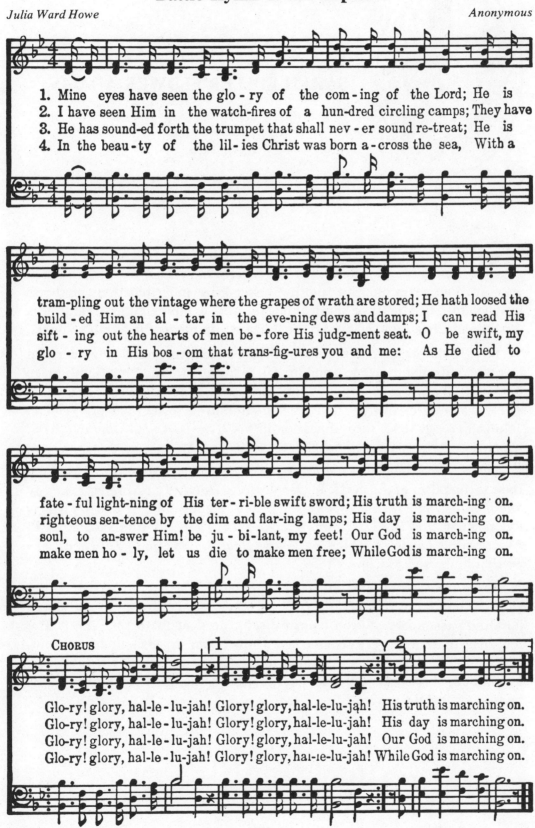

1. Mine eyes have seen the glo - ry of the com-ing of the Lord; He is
2. I have seen Him in the watch-fires of a hun-dred circling camps; They have
3. He has sound-ed forth the trumpet that shall nev - er sound re-treat; He is
4. In the beau-ty of the lil-ies Christ was born a-cross the sea, With a

tram-pling out the vintage where the grapes of wrath are stored; He hath loosed the
build - ed Him an al - tar in the eve-ning dews and damps; I can read His
sift - ing out the hearts of men be - fore His judg-ment seat. O be swift, my
glo - ry in His bos - om that trans-fig-ures you and me: As He died to

fate - ful light-ning of His ter - ri-ble swift sword; His truth is march-ing on.
righteous sen-tence by the dim and flar-ing lamps; His day is march-ing on.
soul, to an-swer Him! be ju - bi-lant, my feet! Our God is march-ing on.
make men ho - ly, let us die to make men free; While God is march-ing on.

CHORUS

Glo-ry! glory, hal-le - lu-jah! Glory! glory, hal-le-lu-jah! His truth is marching on.
Glo-ry! glory, hal-le - lu-jah! Glory! glory, hal-le-lu-jah! His day is marching on.
Glo-ry! glory, hal-le - lu-jah! Glory! glory, hal-le-lu-jah! Our God is marching on.
Glo-ry! glory, hal-le - lu-jah! Glory! glory, hal-le-lu-jah! While God is marching on.

SARAH FULLER FLOWER ADAMS

February 22, 1805 - August 14, 1848

Sarah was born in Harlow, England, daughter of Benjamin Flower, editor of *The Cambridge Intelligencer*. Her mother died when Sarah was only five years old. She and her sister Eliza inherited their mother's frail health. The talents of Sarah and Eliza were complementary. Sarah was a poet and Eliza a musician. Often, Eliza wrote music for Sarah's songs.

In 1834 Sarah married William Bridges Adams, a civil engineer and inventor and went to live in London. There Sarah attended the South Place Unitarian Chapel, Finsbury, London. Her great hymn, *Nearer, My God To Thee*, was one of thirteen hymns she submitted to her pastor, William Johnson Fox in 1840, for publication in his *Hymns And Anthems* (1841), which was to be used at their church.

The original music to *Nearer, My God, To Thee* was written by John Dykes (composer of the music for *Holy, Holy, Holy!*, *The King Of Love My Shepherd Is*, and *Jesus, Lover Of My Soul;* among others) and Dykes' is the popular tune for *Nearer, My God, To Thee* in England. But, in America the music to which we sing *Nearer, My God, To Thee* was written by Lowell Mason in 1859.

Few stories are as famous as the sinking of the *Titanic* and how the ship's band played *Nearer, My God, To Thee*, as the *Titanic*, with fifteen hundred passengers still on board, disappeared beneath the waves. But few know that these were also the last words of our assassinated President, William McKinley. As his attending physician leaned over him, McKinley murmured, " 'Nearer, my God, to Thee, E'en though it be a cross,' has been my constant prayer."

Nearer, My God To Thee

Sarah F. Adams   *Lowell Mason*

1. Near - er, my God, to Thee, Near - er to Thee! E'en though it be a cross
2. Though like the wan-der - er, The sun gone down, Dark-ness be o - ver me,
3. There let the way ap - pear, Steps un - to heaven; All that Thou send-est me,

That rais - eth me; Still all my song shall be, Near - er, my
My rest a stone; Yet in my dreams I'd be Near - er, my
In mer - cy given; An - gels to beck - on me Near - er, my

God, to Thee, Near - er, my God, to Thee, Near - er to Thee!
God, to Thee, Near - er, my God, to Thee, Near - er to Thee!
God, to Thee, Near - er, my God, to Thee, Near - er to Thee! A - MEN.

4 Then, with my waking thoughts
  Bright with Thy praise,
Out of my stony griefs
  Bethel I'll raise;
So by my woes to be
Nearer, my God, to Thee,
  Nearer to Thee!

5 Or if, on joyful wing
  Cleaving the sky.
Sun, moon, and stars forgot,
  Upward I fly,
Still all my song shall be,
Nearer, my God, to Thee,
  Nearer to Thee!

In America, *Nearer My God, To Thee* is sung to the music composed by
Lowell Mason whose biography appears on page 100.

THOMAS HASTINGS

October 15, 1784 - May 15, 1872

The music to which we sing *Guide Me, O Thou Great Jehovah* was written by Thomas Hastings. Born in Washington, Connecticut, Thomas Hastings was an albino and very nearsighted. At the age of twelve his family moved by ox cart to Clinton, New York. By the time he was eighteen Thomas lead the choir of their country church, having taught himself the basics of music.

Thomas Hastings moved to New York City in 1832 at the invitation of twelve different churches who wanted him to lead their choirs. Together with Lowell Mason, Hastings did much to develop church music in America in the 1800's. Through his more than six hundred hymns, one thousand hymn tunes and fifty odd collections, Thomas Hastings made an indelible imprint on the music of his day.

WILLIAM WILLIAMS

February 11, 1717 - January 11, 1791

William Williams, "Father of the modern Welsh hymn", was born in Cefn-y-coed, Wales. He was educated at Llwynllwyd Academy, Carmarthen, for the medical profession, but a sermon by Howell Harris, preaching in Talgarth churchyard, made him decide to enter the ministry.

Williams was ordained a deacon in the Established Church at the age of twenty-three but was refused ordination in 1743 as a priest because of his evangelical ideas. He left the Established Church and became an evangelist of the Welsh Calvinistic Methodist Church.

During his forty-five year ministry, Williams of Pantycelyn (the family farm, "Holy Dell") traveled ninety thousand miles on horseback, preaching throughout Wales and was largely responsible for Methodism's success in Wales, through the great popularity of his hymns.

Guide Me, O Thou Great Jehovah

William Williams   *Thomas Hastings*

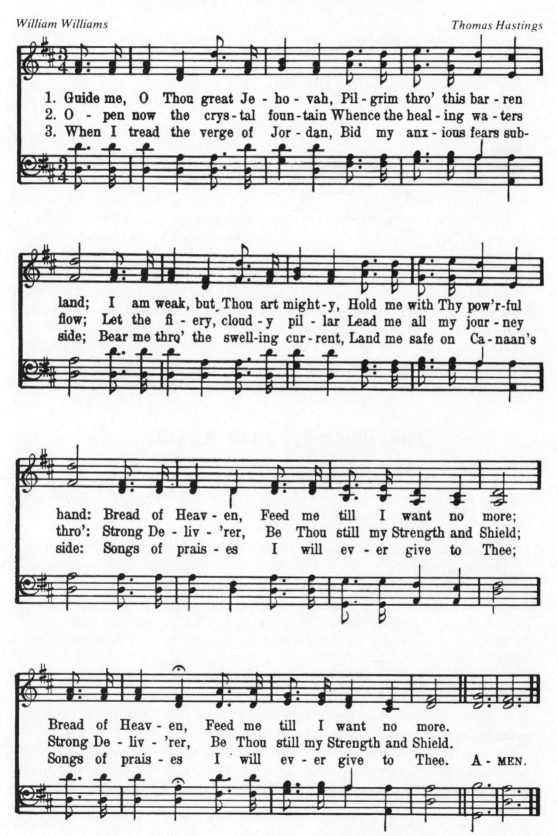

1. Guide me, O Thou great Je - ho - vah, Pil - grim thro' this bar - ren
2. O - pen now the crys - tal foun - tain Whence the heal - ing wa - ters
3. When I tread the verge of Jor - dan, Bid my anx - ious fears sub-

land; I am weak, but Thou art might - y, Hold me with Thy pow'r-ful
flow; Let the fi - er - y, cloud - y pil - lar Lead me all my jour - ney
side; Bear me thro' the swell - ing cur - rent, Land me safe on Ca - naan's

hand: Bread of Heav - en, Feed me till I want no more;
thro': Strong De - liv - 'rer, Be Thou still my Strength and Shield;
side: Songs of prais - es I will ev - er give to Thee;

Bread of Heav - en, Feed me till I want no more.
Strong De - liv - 'rer, Be Thou still my Strength and Shield.
Songs of prais - es I will ev - er give to Thee. A - MEN.

ELIZABETH CECILIA CLEPHANE

June 18, 1830 - February 19, 1869

Elizabeth Cecilia Clephane didn't live to see her beautiful hymn, *Beneath The Cross Of Jesus* published, as she died when only thirty-nine years old.

Elizabeth was born in Edinburgh, Scotland. Her father Andrew was the Sheriff of Fife. After his death, the family moved to Melrose, where Elizabeth earned the nickname, "Sunbeam" from her work in behalf of the poor.

Of her works, eight poems were published in the *Family Treasury,* a Scotch Presbyterian magazine. The first appeared in 1872 and the others in following years, between 1872 and 1874.

FREDERICK CHARLES MAKER

1844 - 1927

Frederick Maker was born in Bristol, England, and spent his entire life there. He began his musical career, as did so many other composers, as a chorister. After studying organ under Alfred Stone, he served as organist at the Milk Street Free Methodist Church. Later, he moved to the Clifton Downs Congregational Church and in 1882, the Redland Congregational Church, where he stayed until his retirement in 1910.

During his career, Maker was also visiting professor at Clifton College and conductor of the Bristol Free Church Choir Association. In 1881, he contributed a number of hymn tunes to *The Bristol Tune Book*, which established him as a hymn tune composer.

Of our *101 Famous Hymns* Frederick Maker wrote the music to which we sing both Elizabeth Clephane's *Beneath The Cross Of Jesus* and John Greenleaf Whittier's *Dear Lord And Father Of Mankind* (page 99.)

Beneath The Cross Of Jesus

Elizabeth C. Clephane　　　　　　　　　　　　　　　　　　　　　　*Frederick C. Maker*

1. Be - neath the cross of Je - sus I fain would take my stand,
2. Up - on that cross of Je - sus Mine eye at times can see
3. I take, O cross, thy shad - ow For my a - bid - ing place;

The shad - ow of a might - y rock With - in a wea - ry land;
The ver - y dy - ing form of One Who suf - fered there for me;
I ask no oth - er sun - shine than The sun - shine of His face;

A home with - in the wil - der - ness, A rest up - on the way,
And from my strick - en heart with tears Two won - ders I con - fess:
Con - tent to let the world go by, To know no gain nor loss,

From the burn - ing of the noon - tide heat, And the bur - den of the day.
The won - ders of re - deem - ing love And my un - wor - thi - ness.
My sin - ful self my on - ly shame, My glo - ry all the cross. A - MEN.

97

JOHN GREENLEAF WHITTIER

December 17, 1807 - September 7, 1892

The Quaker Poet'' as he was often called, was born in 1807, in a house built by his great-grandfather in 1688, near Haverhill, Massachusetts. John's early life was hard. His parents were very poor and he received little formal education until working as a shoemaker and teacher he saved enough money to enter Haverhill Academy when he was nineteen. Here, Whittier found for the first time a library. Until then his only book of verse had been Robert Burn's *Poems*.

When Whittier began to write verse his older sister sent it to the noted publisher of his day, William Lloyd Garrison, who took an immediate interest in Whittier. By the time he was twenty-five, Whittier had made a reputation for himself as a writer and also had achieved some success in politics. The slavery issue however, was one young John could not evade; he was foursquare against it and this ended all ideas of a political career.

Whittier became editor of the *American Manufacturer* in 1828, the *New England Review* in 1830, the *Pennsylvania Freeman* in 1836 where mobs burned his offices for his anti-slavery writing and in 1847 he joined the editorial staff of the *National Era*, the journal that first published, in serial form, *Uncle Tom's Cabin*.

Whittier's works range from, *The Barefoot Boy, With Cheek Of Tan* to *Our Master* and are too numerous to be listed here. Whittier did not consider himself a hymn writer, as Quakers never sang in their meetings, but his poetry had such a lyric quality that at least seventy-five centos, drawn from his poems, have been made into hymns, including the most loved hymn, *Dear Lord And Father Of Mankind*.

The music to which we sing *Dear Lord And Father Of Mankind* was written by Charles Frederick Maker who also wrote the music for *Beneath The Cross Of Jesus*. His biography appears with that of its author Elizabeth Clephane, on page 96.

98

Dear Lord and Father of Mankind

John G. Whittier   *Frederick C. Maker*

1. Dear Lord and Fa - ther of man - kind. For - give our fool - ish
2. In sim - ple trust like theirs who heard. Be - side the Syr - ian
3. Drop Thy still dews of qui - et - ness, Till all our striv - ings
4. Breathe through the heats of our de - sire Thy cool - ness and Thy

ways! Re - clothe us in our right - ful mind; In pur - er
sea The gra - cious call - ing of the Lord. Let us like
cease; Take from our souls the strain and stress, And let our
balm; Let sense be dumb, let flesh re - tire; Speak through the

lives Thy serv - ice find, In deep - er rev - 'rence, praise.
them, with - out a word. Rise up and fol - low Thee.
or - dered lives con - fess The beau - ty of Thy peace.
earth - quake, wind, and fire, O still small voice of calm! A - MEN.

This prayer, Dear Lord And Father Of Mankind, forms the concluding stanzas of Whittier's poem, The Brewing of Soma, in which he describes the East Indian drinkers of the intoxicating Soma who hope thereby to approach God.

RAY PALMER

November 12, 1808 - March 29, 1887

ay Palmer was born in Little Compton, Rhode Island, the son of Judge Thomas Palmer. He spent his boyhood in Boston where he worked as a clerk in a dry-goods store. Upon graduation from Yale in 1830, he began to study theology while teaching at a girls school in New York. It was while teaching at this school that the hymn, *My Faith Looks Up To Thee*, came upon him and seemed to write itself in a moment of quietude.

Ordained in 1835, he became pastor of the Central Congregational Church in Bath, Maine. Fifteen years later he accepted a call to the First Congregational Church of Albany, New York. This pastorate also lasted fifteen years, for in 1865 he was appointed Corresponding Secretary in New York City for the American Congregational Union, a position he held until his retirement in 1878.

During Ray Palmer's career he wrote several books of poetry and hymns and upon request, contributed a number of excellent hymns to the *Sabbath Hymn Book* of 1858. During his life, Dr. Palmer permitted no one, not even his friend Lowell Mason, to revise the text of his hymns nor would he accept a royalty on their sale.

LOWELL MASON

July 8, 1792 - August 11, 1872

he fierce battle between those who believed only psalms should be sung and those who wanted hymns was, in part, finally decided in the United States by the work of Lowell Mason, Thomas Hastings and **William Bradbury.** **(Continued on page 102.)**

My Faith Looks Up To Thee

Ray Palmer   *Lowell Mason*

1. My faith looks up to Thee, Thou Lamb of Cal - va - ry,
2. May Thy rich grace im - part Strength to my faint - ing heart,
3. While life's dark maze I tread, And griefs a - round me spread,
4. When ends life's tran - sient dream, When death's cold, sul - len stream

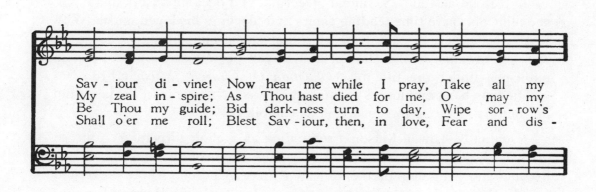

Sav - iour di - vine! Now hear me while I pray, Take all my
My zeal in - spire; As Thou hast died for me, O may my
Be Thou my guide; Bid dark - ness turn to day, Wipe sor - row's
Shall o'er me roll; Blest Sav - iour, then, in love, Fear and dis -

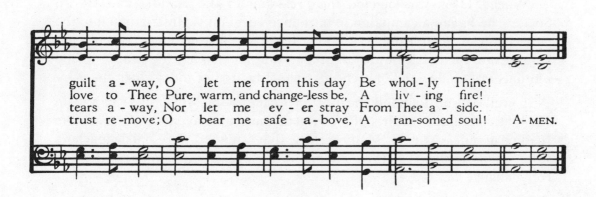

guilt a - way, O let me from this day Be whol - ly Thine!
love to Thee Pure, warm, and change - less be, A liv - ing fire!
tears a - way, Nor let me ev - er stray From Thee a - side.
trust re - move; O bear me safe a - bove, A ran - somed soul! A - MEN.

LOWELL MASON

July 8, 1792 - August 11, 1872

(Lowell Mason's biography continued from page 100.)

(Lowell Mason's biography continued from page 100.)

Lowell Mason was born in Medfield, Massachusetts, where he learned to play every kind of musical instrument. At the age of sixteen he became a choir leader and instructor of singing classes.

In 1815 he moved to Savannah, Georgia, and became a clerk in a bank, spending his spare time leading choirs and teaching his loved music. With F. L. Abel he prepared a book of choral music and through George K. Jackson, organist of the Handel and Haydn Society, convinced them to publish it under the title of *Collection Of Church Music* (1818). Not wanting his bank employers to think of him as a "music man", Mason did not put his name on the collection as compiler.

Eventually, Lowell Mason's reputation as a choir director became so great he moved to Boston, taking charge of three church choirs. Later he became choir director of the Bowdoin Street Church, where Reverend Lyman Beecher, father of Henry Ward Beecher and Harriet Beecher Stowe, was pastor. Here, Lowell Mason began music classes for the children and published *The Juvenile Psalmist*.

When Mason was elected the president of the Handel and Haydn Society he began a campaign to introduce vocal music instruction into the curriculum of Boston public schools. In 1838 Boston public schools put singing into the curriculum "in preparation for making the praise of God glorious in families and churches" (school boards of today, take note).

Lowell Mason founded the Boston Academy of Music in 1832 and in 1834 he conducted the first of his famous musical conventions to teach the reading of music by note. Many of those that attended were music teachers who upon return to their hometowns organized similar teaching conventions.

During his career, Mason was associated in the publication of at least eighty collections of music, composed hundreds of tunes, and was editor and publisher of the *New York Musical Review*.

Lowell Mason was the first American to receive a Doctorate in Music from an American university. The year was 1835 and the school, New York University.

How Firm A Foundation

"K" in Rippon's Selection, 1787   *From John F. Wade's Cantus Diversi, 1751*

1. How firm a foun-da-tion, ye saints of the Lord, Is laid for your
2. "Fear not, I am with thee; O be not dis-mayed, For I am thy
3. "When thro' the deep wa-ters I call thee to go, The riv-ers of

faith in His ex-cel-lent Word! What more can He say than to
God, and will still give thee aid; I'll strength-en thee, help thee, and
woe shall not thee o-ver-flow; For I will be with thee thy

you He hath said, To you who for ref-uge to Je-sus have fled?
cause thee to stand, Up-held by my right-eous, om-nip-o-tent hand,
trou-bles to bless, And sanc-ti-fy to thee thy deep-est dis-tress,

To you who for ref-uge to Je-sus have fled?
Up-held by my right-eous, om-nip-o-tent hand.
And sanc-ti-fy to thee thy deep-est dis-tress. A-MEN.

How Firm A Foundation, signed only with the letter "K" was taken
from John Rippon's famous hymn collection, *Selection Of Hymns From
The Best Authors*. **John Rippon's biography appears on page 68.**

HARRIET BEECHER STOWE

June 14, 1811 - July 1, 1896

Only her fame as the author of *Uncle Tom's Cabin* overshadows her hymn writing greatness, for few hymns can match the poetic beauty of *Still, Still With Thee.*

Harriet Beecher Stowe was born in Litchfield, Connecticut. Her father was Dr. Lyman Beecher, a distinguished minister and all six of her brothers became ministers, with the youngest of them becoming the famous Henry Ward Beecher.

In 1832 the family moved to Cincinnati, Ohio, when Dr. Beecher became president of Lane Theological Seminary. Here Harriet met and married a member of the faculty, professor Calvin E. Stowe. Both she and Calvin held strong views against slavery and soon their Cincinnati home became one of the stations for the ''underground railroad''.

Life was not easy for the Stowes. In 1849, with her husband broken in health and in an Eastern sanatorium, her infant son died during a cholera epidemic in Cincinnati. Eight years later the oldest son, Henry, drowned. Then came the Civil War where their third son, Fred, was wounded at Gettysburg permanently damaging his brain. In addition, before Harriet wrote *Uncle Tom's Cabin*, there were always financial problems. Professor Stowe had moved his family to Brunswick, Maine to accept a position at Bowdoin College but with five children a teacher's pay was just not sufficient. In order to help meet expenses Harriet wrote articles for the *National Era* magazine.

In February of 1851, while attending a communion service, the death scene from *Uncle Tom's Cabin* passed before her mind. When she returned home she immediately began writing *Uncle Tom's Cabin* which appeared in serial form in the *National Era*, beginning June 5, 1851. Almost overnight, Harriet Beecher Stowe became famous and the specter of poverty banished forever.

Not long before her death at the age of eighty-four she wrote a friend:
''Tis joy enough, my All in all,
At Thy dear feet to lie.
Thou wilt not let me lower fall,
And none can higher fly.''

The biography of the composer, Felix Mendelssohn, appears on page 46.

Still, Still With Thee

Harriet B. Stowe

Arr. from Felix Mendelssohn-Bartholdy

1. Still, still with Thee, when pur - ple morn - ing break - eth,
2. A - lone with Thee, a - mid the mys - tic shad - ows,
3. Still, still with Thee! As to each new - born morn - ing
4. When sinks the soul, sub - dued by toil, to slum - ber,
5. So shall it be at last, in that bright morn - ing,

When the bird wak - eth, and the shad - ows flee;
The sol - emn hush of na - ture new - ly born;
A fresh and sol - emn splen - dor still is given,
Its clos - ing eyes look up to Thee in prayer;
When the soul wak - eth, and life's shad - ows flee;

Fair - er than morn - ing, love - li - er than day - light,
A - lone with Thee in breath - less ad - o - ra - tion,
So does this bless - ed con - scious - ness, a - wak - ing,
Sweet the re - pose be - neath Thy wings o'er - shad - ing,
O in that hour, fair - er than day - light dawn - ing,

Dawns the swect con - scious - ness, I am with Thee.
In the calm dew and fresh - ness ' of the morn.
Breathe each day near - ness un - to Thee and heaven.
But sweet - er still, to wake and find Thee there.
Shall rise the glo - rious thought, I am with Thee. A - MEN.

105

JOHN ZUNDEL

December 10, 1815 - July, 1882

The first major hymnal with the music printed on the same page as the words, was edited by John Zundel and Charles Beecher when Zundel was organist at Henry Ward Beecher's famous Plymouth Congregational Church in Brooklyn, New York. The name of this famous hymnal was the *Plymouth Collection,* the date 1855. It was regarded as a very controversial work because it combined hymns of many faiths including Moravian and Roman Catholic and no publisher would finance it. Finally, two church members paid for it. Realizing it would be attacked, Reverend Henry Ward Beecher wrote:

"Some of the most touching and truly evangelical hymns have been gathered from Roman Catholic sources. It has been a joy to us to learn, during our research, how much food for true piety is afforded through Catholic books."

This boldness aroused a storm of criticism but the *Plymouth Collection* became a best seller.

John Zundel was born in 1815 at Hochdorf, Germany. He began his professional career as organist at St. Anne's Lutheran Church and as bandmaster of the Imperial Horse Guards in St. Petersburg (now Leningrad, Russia). He came to the United States in 1847. After playing briefly at other churches he began his great career at the Plymouth Church in Brooklyn on January 1, 1850. Here, with the famous Henry Ward Beecher, the great orator, they drew not only New Yorkers, but hundreds of visitors from other states, Sunday after Sunday. Attending the Plymouth Church in Brooklyn was an experience to write home about, with Beecher's powerful sermons, Zundel's inspired organ playing and the best congregational singing of its day. A picture of historic Plymouth Church appears on page 123.

While in the United States John Zundel published three books of music. Of his last, *Christian Heart Songs* (1870), Zundel said, "It has required almost a lifetime to compose its contents". In 1877 John Zundel retired and returned to his native land.

The biography of Charles Wesley, author of *Love Divine, All Love Excelling,* appears on page 38.

Love Divine

Charles Wesley
John Zundel

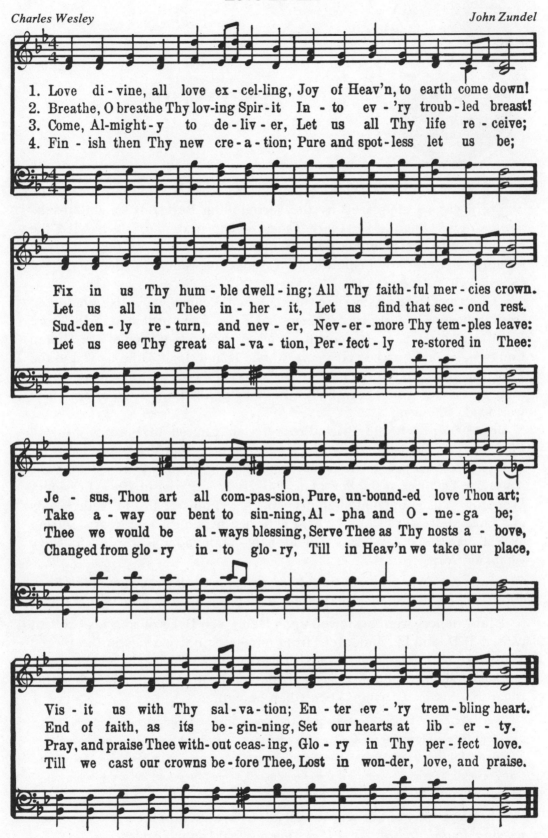

1. Love di-vine, all love ex-cel-ling, Joy of Heav'n, to earth come down!
2. Breathe, O breathe Thy lov-ing Spir-it In-to ev-'ry troub-led breast!
3. Come, Al-might-y to de-liv-er, Let us all Thy life re-ceive;
4. Fin-ish then Thy new cre-a-tion; Pure and spot-less let us be;

Fix in us Thy hum-ble dwell-ing; All Thy faith-ful mer-cies crown.
Let us all in Thee in-her-it, Let us find that sec-ond rest.
Sud-den-ly re-turn, and nev-er, Nev-er-more Thy tem-ples leave:
Let us see Thy great sal-va-tion, Per-fect-ly re-stored in Thee:

Je-sus, Thou art all com-pas-sion, Pure, un-bound-ed love Thou art;
Take a-way our bent to sin-ning, Al-pha and O-me-ga be;
Thee we would be al-ways blessing, Serve Thee as Thy hosts a-bove,
Changed from glo-ry in-to glo-ry, Till in Heav'n we take our place,

Vis-it us with Thy sal-va-tion; En-ter ev-'ry trem-bling heart.
End of faith, as its be-gin-ning, Set our hearts at lib-er-ty.
Pray, and praise Thee with-out ceas-ing, Glo-ry in Thy per-fect love.
Till we cast our crowns be-fore Thee, Lost in won-der, love, and praise.

HENRY van DYKE

November 10, 1852 - April 10, 1933

When Henry van Dyke was a guest preacher at Williams College, he was so impressed by the surrounding Berkshire mountains he wrote *Joyful, Joyful, We Adore Thee* and the next morning handed the manuscript to President Garfield saying, "Here is a hymn for you. Your mountains were my inspiration. It must be sung to the music of 'Beethoven's, Hymn to Joy.' "

Henry van Dyke was born in Germantown, Pennsylvania. He graduated from Princeton Theological Seminary in 1877 and was ordained in 1879 as a Presbyterian minister. He began his great career as pastor of the United Congregational Church in Newport, Rhode Island. In 1883 he moved to the Brick Presbyterian Church in New York City, where he remained for seventeen years and wrote seven books, his mastery of English creating a vast worldwide following.

In 1899 he left the Brick Presbyterian Church to become Murray Professor of English Literature at Princeton, a position he held for twenty-three years, with frequent interruptions. From 1908 to 1909 he was American Lecturer at the Sorbonne University in Paris. In 1913, President Woodrow Wilson appointed Henry van Dyke minister to the Netherlands and Luxemburg, a position he held with distinction for four years. During WW I, van Dyke served as a lieutenant-commander in the U. S. Navy Chaplain Corps.

It was van Dyke who was largely responsible for the revision of the *Book Of Common Prayer*, adopted by the Presbyterian Church in 1931.

Many honors were bestowed upon Henry van Dyke during his brilliant career. D.D. and LL.D. degrees from numerous universities in the United States and a D.C.L. from Oxford University in 1917.

There are no better words to sum up Henry van Dyke's thoughts regarding his many hymns then when he wrote:

"These verses are simple expressions of common Christian feelings and desires in this present time, -- hymns of today that may be sung together by people who know the thought of the age, and are not afraid that any truth of science will destroy religion, or any revolution on earth overthrow the kingdom of heaven. Therefore these are hymns of trust and joy and hope."

The biography of Ludwig van Beethoven, author of the music to which we sing *Joyful, Joyful, We Adore Thee*, appears on page 110.

Joyful, Joyful, We Adore Thee

Henry van Dyke   *Ludwig van Beethoven*

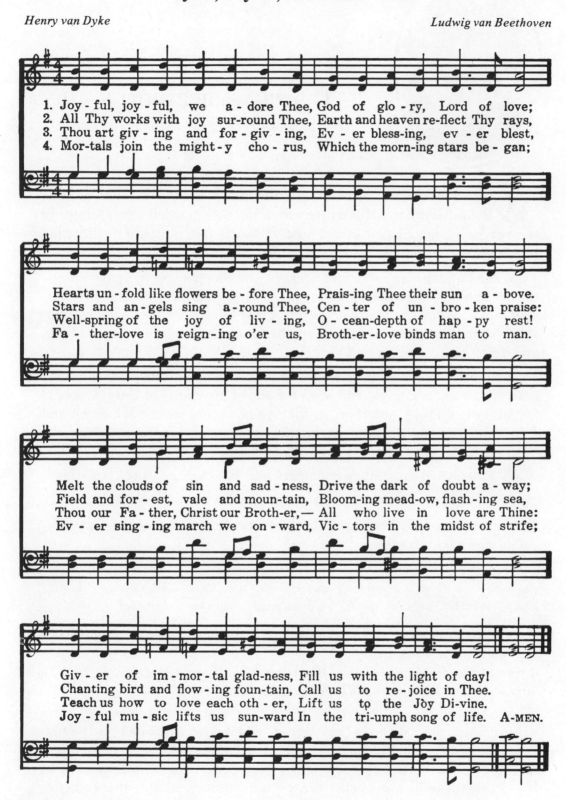

1. Joy-ful, joy-ful, we a-dore Thee, God of glo-ry, Lord of love;
2. All Thy works with joy sur-round Thee, Earth and heaven re-flect Thy rays,
3. Thou art giv-ing and for-giv-ing, Ev-er bless-ing, ev-er blest,
4. Mor-tals join the might-y cho-rus, Which the morn-ing stars be-gan;

Hearts un-fold like flowers be-fore Thee, Prais-ing Thee their sun a-bove.
Stars and an-gels sing a-round Thee, Cen-ter of un-bro-ken praise:
Well-spring of the joy of liv-ing, O-cean-depth of hap-py rest!
Fa-ther-love is reign-ing o'er us, Broth-er-love binds man to man.

Melt the clouds of sin and sad-ness, Drive the dark of doubt a-way;
Field and for-est, vale and moun-tain, Bloom-ing mead-ow, flash-ing sea,
Thou our Fa-ther, Christ our Broth-er,— All who live in love are Thine:
Ev-er sing-ing march we on-ward, Vic-tors in the midst of strife;

Giv-er of im-mor-tal glad-ness, Fill us with the light of day!
Chanting bird and flow-ing foun-tain, Call us to re-joice in Thee.
Teach us how to love each oth-er, Lift us to the Joy Di-vine.
Joy-ful mu-sic lifts us sun-ward In the tri-umph song of life. A-MEN.

LUDWIG van BEETHOVEN

December 16, 1770 - March 26, 1827

The "Shakespeare of music", Ludwig van Beethoven, was born in Bonn, Germany. His father was a highly regarded tenor singer in the service of the Elector of Cologne at Bonn but his father's drinking problem kept the family poverty striken.

When Ludwig was only eight years old he was playing in public and by the time he was ten, composing music. At the age of seventeen the Elector sent him to Vienna to study under the great Mozart, but his stay was cut short when after three months he rushed back to Bonn due to the illness and death of his mother and sister.

A fiercely independent person Beethoven decided to free lance rather than do as most musicians and work for one of the courts of Europe, as did his father and his grandfather. At the age of twenty-two he left Bonn and settled in Vienna. Here he began his studies in composition from the "Father of the Symphony", Franz Joseph Haydn, and Albrechtsberger.

In 1801, when only thirty-one years old, Beethoven wrote to a friend:

"For two years I have avoided almost all society because I cannot tell people, I am deaf."

Later that same year he wrote this statement regarding his music and his relationship with God:

"No friend have I. I must live by myself alone; but I know well that God is nearer to me than to others in my art, so I walk fearlessly with Him. I have always known Him and understood Him. I have no timidity about my music; it can have no ill fate ..."

While Beethoven did not write any hymn music as such, the music for many hymns has been adapted from his larger works, such as that chosen by van Dyke for *Joyful, Joyful We Adore Thee* (page 109) from the *Ode To Joy* section of Beethoven's *Ninth Symphony.*

Without question Beethoven's *Ninth Symphony* was the *magnum opus* of his great career. When in February of 1824 it was performed for the first time the audience in Vienna greeted it with thunderous applause, however Beethoven now totally deaf could not hear it. Instead he stood gazing at the orchestra until a musician turned him around. When the audience realized that Beethoven could not hear their applause, they rose from their seats to wave their arms and handkerchiefs. Beethoven, although unable to hear a sound, had created a musical masterpiece.

Away In A Manger

Anonymous

19th century, American

1. A-way in a man-ger, no crib for his bed, The lit-tle Lord

Je-sus laid down his sweet head; The stars in the sky looked

down where he lay, The lit-tle Lord Je-sus, a-sleep on the hay. A-men.

2 The cattle are lowing, the poor baby wakes,
But little Lord Jesus no crying he makes.
I love thee, Lord Jesus, look down from the sky,
And stay by my cradle to watch lullaby.

3 Be near me, Lord Jesus; I ask thee to stay
Close by me for ever, and love me, I pray.
Bless all the dear children in thy tender care,
And fit us for heaven, to live with thee there.   Amen.

MALTBIE DAVENPORT BABCOCK

August 3, 1858 - May 18, 1901

altbie Babcock, author of *This Is My Father's World*, was born in Syracuse, New York, into a socially prominent family. He was educated at Syracuse University and Auburn Theological Seminary. In school he was a great athlete, an actor and a musician.

After ordination as a Presbyterian minister, he was called to the Presbyterian Church in Lockport, New York. In 1886 he became pastor of the prestigious Brown Memorial Church in Baltimore. After almost fourteen years Babcock left Brown Memorial to fill the vacancy at the Brick Presbyterian Church in New York City, created by the retirement of the noted Henry Van Dyke.

Maltbie Babcock's great career was cut short in 1901, just eighteen months after becoming pastor of the Brick Presbyterian Church. As he and his wife were returning from a visit to the Holy Land, Maltbie Babcock died. Most of his hymns were published after his death, including the most loved hymn, *This Is My Father's World*.

FRANKLIN LAWRENCE SHEPPARD

August 7, 1852 - February 15, 1930

ranklin was born in Philadelphia and prepared for college at the Classical School of William Fewsmith. He graduated from the University of Pennsylvania at the head of his class in 1872. In 1875 his father, president of Isaac A. Sheppard & Co., a stove and heater manufacturer, sent him to Boston to take charge of its foundry.

Here, Franklin joined the Zion Protestant Episcopal Church and was elected vestryman. Later he became a Presbyterian and joined the Second Presbyterian Church in Baltimore, serving as a member of the Session, a Sunday school teacher and director of music. Eventually, he became president of the Presbyterian Board of Publications and Sabbath-School Works.

Franklin was an accomplished musician and edited, *Alleluia*, a Presbyterian Sunday school song-book published in 1915 which sold almost one half million copies. It was in *Alleluia* that Franklin Sheppard published many of Babcock's hymns including *This Is My Father's World*.

This Is My Father's World

Maltbie D. Babcock

Franklin L. Sheppard

1. This is my Fa-ther's world, And to my list-ening ears, All
2. This is my Fa-ther's world, The birds their car-ols raise, The
3. This is my Fa-ther's world, O let me ne'er for-get That

na - ture sings, and round me rings The mu - sic of the spheres.
morn - ing light, the lil - y white, De - clare their Mak - er's praise.
though the wrong seems oft so strong, God is the Rul - er yet.

This is my Fa-ther's world: I rest me in the thought Of
This is my Fa-ther's world: He shines in all that's fair; In the
This is my Fa-ther's world: Why should my heart be sad? The

rocks and trees, of skies and seas; His hand the won-ders wrought.
rust - ling grass I hear Him pass, He speaks to me ev-ery-where.
Lord is King: let the heav-ens ring! God reigns: let the earth be glad! A-MEN.

HARRY EMERSON FOSDICK

May 24, 1878 - October 5, 1969

God Of Grace And God Of Glory was written by Harry Emerson Fosdick at his summer home in Maine, for the opening service of the famed Riverside Church, New York City on October 5, 1930.

Born in Buffalo, New York, to a prominent family (they came to Massachusetts from England in 1635) Fosdick was educated at Colgate University, Union Theological Seminary and Columbia University (M.A. 1908).

His first pastorate was the First Baptist Church, Montclair, New Jersey, from 1904 to 1915. While serving there he also taught homiletics at Union Seminary from 1908 to 1915 and occupied the chair of practial theology at Union, from 1915 to 1946.

During World War I, Fosdick ministered to troops in England and France. Upon return home he accepted a call from the First Presbyterian Church in New York City but left in 1926 because of differing theological concepts.

Fosdick was then approached by John D. Rockefeller, Jr., who offered him the pulpit of New York's prestigious Park Avenue Baptist Church. At first Fosdick refused but finally accepted under these conditions:

1. That they no longer require immersion of those desiring to join;
2. That they grant membership to all Christians regardless of creed;
3. That they build a new church in a less exclusive district; and
4. That they pay the minister no more than $5,000 a year.

The congregation accepted and over the next five years built their new five million dollar neo-Gothic cathedral, the non-denominational, Riverside Church.

Not only did Fosdick fill the two thousand five hundred seats of Riverside Church every Sunday, his sermons broadcast nationally from his eighteenth floor tower study, were heard by millions of Americans. And, more millions of people, worldwide, were influenced by Fosdick's six books of sermons and twenty-six books on other religious themes, many of which became best sellers and were translated into numerous languages.

The biography of John Hughes, composer of the music to which we sing *God Of Grace And God Of Glory,* appears on page 116.

114

God Of Grace And God Of Glory

Harry Emerson Fosdick

John Hughes

1 God of grace and God of glory, On thy peo-ple
2 Lo! the hosts of e-vil round us Scorn thy Christ, as-
3 Cure thy chil-dren's war-ring mad-ness; Bend our pride to
4 Set our feet on loft-y pla-ces; Gird our lives that
5 Save us from weak res-ig-na-tion To the e-vils

pour thy power; Crown thine an-cient church's sto-ry; Bring her bud to
sail his ways! From the fears that long have bound us, Free our hearts to
thy con-trol; Shame our wan-ton, self-ish glad-ness, Rich in things and
they may be Arm-ored with all Christ-like gra-ces In the fight to
we de-plore; Let the search for thy sal-va-tion Be our glo-ry

glo-rious flower. Grant us wis-dom, Grant us cour-age,
faith and praise. Grant us wis-dom, Grant us cour-age,
poor in soul. Grant us wis-dom, Grant us cour-age,
set men free. Grant us wis-dom, Grant us cour-age,
ev-er-more. Grant us wis-dom, Grant us cour-age,

For the fac-ing of this hour, For the fac-ing of this hour.
For the liv-ing of these days, For the liv-ing of these days.
Lest we miss thy king-dom's goal, Lest we miss thy king-dom's goal.
That we fail not man nor thee, That we fail not man nor thee.
Serv-ing thee whom we a-dore, Serv-ing thee whom we a-dore. A-men.

JOHN HUGHES

1873 - May 14, 1932

Harry Emerson Fosdick's *God Of Grace, God Of Glory* is sung to two tunes. It was first sung to a tune known as *Regent Square*, a tune, published in 1867 in the English Presbyterian hymnal, *Psalms and Hymns For Divine Worship*. In 1935 the Methodists and Baptists adopted the tune named *CWM Rhondda* for *God Of Grace And God Of Glory*. This tune was written by John Hughes in 1907 for a singing festival commemorating anniversary services at Capel Rhondda in Wales.

John, the eldest son of Evan Hughes, was born at Dowlais, Wales. The following year the family moved to Llantwit Fardre. He began work at the age of twelve and rose to an official position with the Great Western Colliery Company.

A gifted composer and an active churchman, John succeeded his father as deacon and precentor of Salem Baptist Church, where he held lifelong membership. John Hughes wrote the tunes of two anthems during his career, a number of Sunday school marches and a great number of hymn tunes.

ROBERT JACKSON

1842 - 1914

Robert Jackson, composer of the music to which we sing *Breathe on Me, Breath of God,* was born in Oldham, England and spent his life there. He was the son of the parish organist at St. Peter's Church. He studied at the Royal Academy of Music and was organist at St. Mark's. Then, in 1868 he succeeded his father at St. Peter's in Oldham. Between father and son the Jacksons served as St. Peter's organist for ninety-six years.

During his career, Robert Jackson wrote many hymn tunes, directed the Oldham Musical Society and the Werneth Vocal Society.

Breathe on Me, Breath of God

Edwin Hatch   Robert Jackson

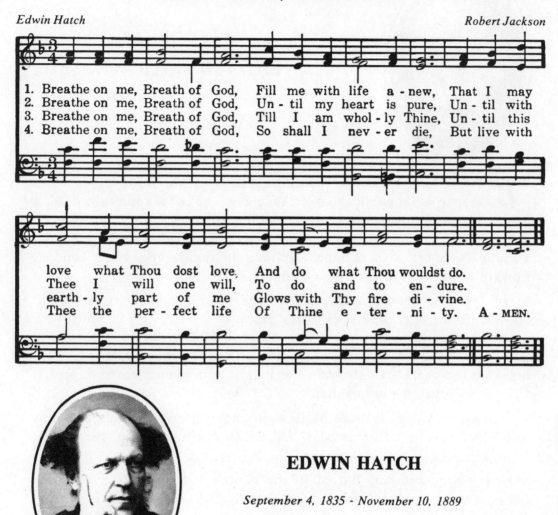

1. Breathe on me, Breath of God, Fill me with life a - new, That I may
2. Breathe on me, Breath of God, Un - til my heart is pure, Un - til with
3. Breathe on me, Breath of God, Till I am whol - ly Thine, Un - til this
4. Breathe on me, Breath of God, So shall I nev - er die, But live with

love   what Thou dost love, And do   what Thou wouldst do.
Thee   I   will one will, To do   and to en - dure.
earth - ly   part of   me   Glows with Thy fire di - vine.
Thee   the per - fect life Of Thine e - ter - ni - ty. A - MEN.

EDWIN HATCH

September 4, 1835 - November 10, 1889

The author of *Breathe On Me, Breath Of God*, Edwin Hatch, was born in Derby, England, and educated at King Edward's School and at Pembroke College, Oxford (A.B. 1857). In 1853 he joined the Church of England and in 1859 was ordained a priest. After serving briefly as a parish priest in East London, he moved to Toronto, Canada, where he became professor of classics at Trinity College and later, from 1859 to 1866, served as rector of a high school in Quebec, Canada. In 1867 he returned to England as vice president of St. Mary's Hall at Oxford. In 1883 Hatch became rector at Purleigh and two years later university reader in ecclesiastical history, where he served with distinction until his death in 1889. A scholar of renown, Edwin Hatch, was widely acclaimed in Europe for his Bampton Lectures of 1880 and Hibbert Lectures of 1888.

EDWARD MOTE

January 21, 1797 - November 13, 1874

Edward Mote was born in London, England, where his father was a keeper of a public house. As a boy, he was apprenticed to a cabinetmaker. He began to attend church and was greatly influenced by John Hyatt, a preacher at one of Lady Huntingdon's chapels, the Tottenham Court Road Chapel. Settling in Southwark, near London, Edward Mote went to work as a cabinetmaker.

In 1847 he became a Baptist minister and preached at Horsham, Sussex, for the next twenty-six years. Because the building in which they worshiped had been secured largely through Mote's efforts, the congregation offered to give him title to the property but he refused saying, "I do not want the chapel, I only want the pulpit; and when I cease to preach Christ, then turn me out of that."

During his career Edward Mote wrote more than one hundred hymns which were published in his book *Hymns Of Praise* (London, 1836).

Edward Mote retired in 1873 due to failing health. He died the following year and was buried in the churchyard, but his hymn *The Immutable Basis Of A Sinner's Hope* (*The Solid Rock*) lives on.

WILLIAM BATCHELDER BRADBURY

October 6, 1816 - January 7, 1868

The music to *The Solid Rock* was composed by William B. Bradbury in 1863 and published in his, *The Devotional Hymn And Tune Book* (1864). The biography of William Batchelder Bradbury appears on page 136.

The Solid Rock

Edward Mote

William B. Bradbury

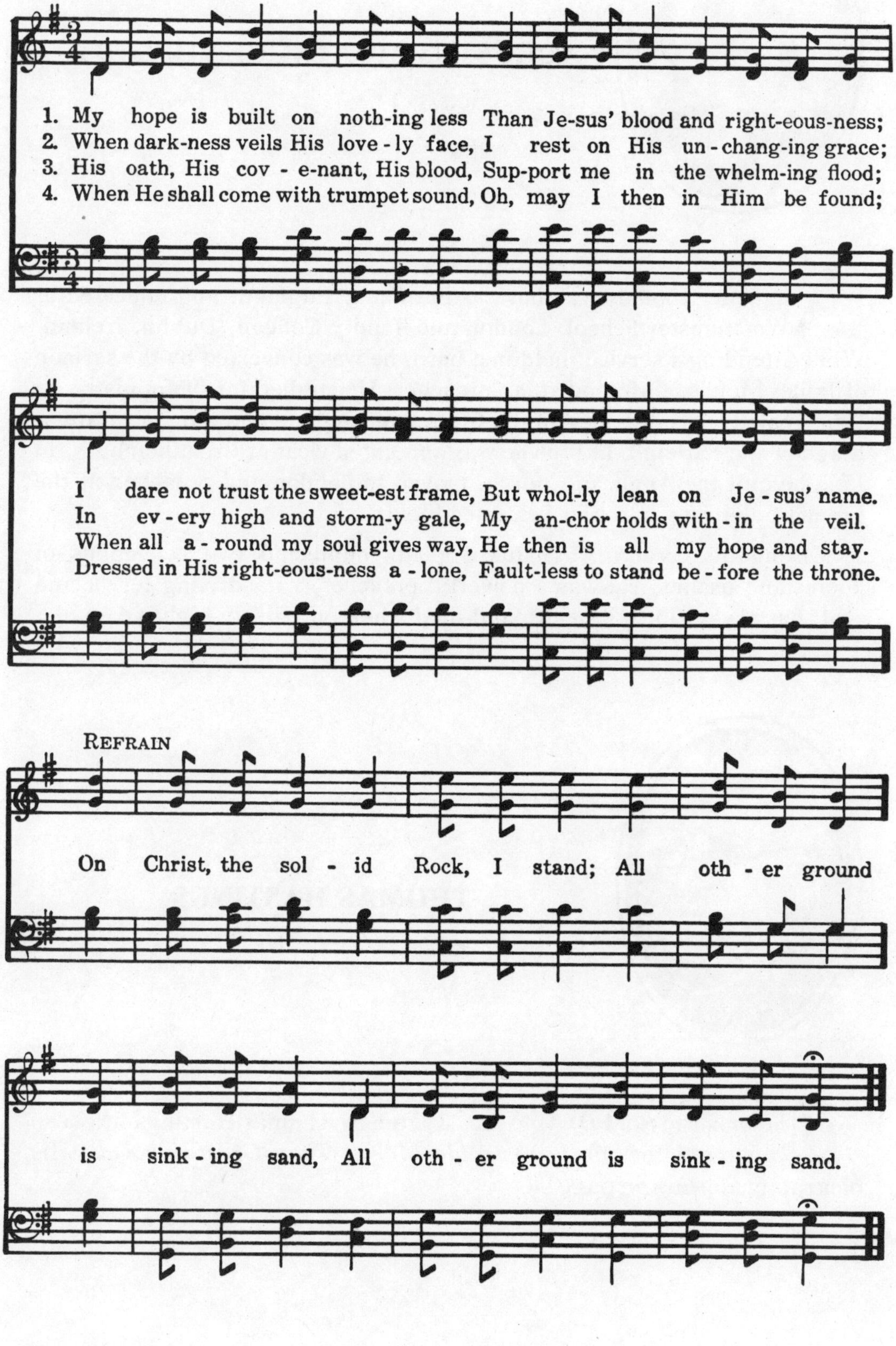

1. My hope is built on noth-ing less Than Je-sus' blood and right-eous-ness;
2. When dark-ness veils His love-ly face, I rest on His un-chang-ing grace;
3. His oath, His cov-e-nant, His blood, Sup-port me in the whelm-ing flood;
4. When He shall come with trumpet sound, Oh, may I then in Him be found;

I dare not trust the sweet-est frame, But whol-ly lean on Je-sus' name.
In ev-ery high and storm-y gale, My an-chor holds with-in the veil.
When all a-round my soul gives way, He then is all my hope and stay.
Dressed in His right-eous-ness a-lone, Fault-less to stand be-fore the throne.

REFRAIN

On Christ, the sol-id Rock, I stand; All oth-er ground is sink-ing sand, All oth-er ground is sink-ing sand.

119

AUGUSTUS MONTAGUE TOPLADY

November 4, 1740 - August 11, 1778

Augustus Toplady was born at Farnham, England, and educated at Westminster School, London and Trinity College, Dublin, Ireland. While attending a service, held in a barn, he was converted by the sermon of James Morris, a Methodist lay preacher. He studied for the ministry. In 1762 Toplady was ordained in the Church of England and named curate at Blagdon and Farleigh. In 1766 he was appointed vicar at Broadhembury. In 1775 he quit the Anglican Church, moved to London and preached at the French Calvinist Church in Leicester Fields.

During his career Augustus Toplady published two collections of poems and psalms. He was a powerful preacher, with driving fervor and zeal but always in frail health and died when only thirty-eight years old.

THOMAS HASTINGS

October 15, 1784 - May 15, 1872

The music to *Rock Of Ages* was written by Thomas Hastings who also composed the music to *Guide Me, O Thou Great Jehovah*. His biography appears on page 94.

Rock Of Ages

Augustus M. Toplady   *Thomas Hastings*

1. Rock of A - ges, cleft for me, Let me hide my-self in thee;
2. Not the la - bors of my hands Can ful - fill thy law's de - mands;

Let the wa - ter and the blood, From thy riv - en side which flowed,
Could my zeal no res - pite know, Could my tears for ev - er flow,

Be of sin the dou - ble cure, Cleanse me from its guilt and power.
All for sin could not a - tone; Thou must save, and thou a - lone. A-men.

3 Nothing in my hand I bring,
   Simply to thy Cross I cling;
   Naked, come to thee for dress;
   Helpless, look to thee for grace;
   Foul, I to the fountain fly;
   Wash me, Saviour, or I die.

4 While I draw this fleeting breath,
   When mine eyelids close in death,
   When I soar to worlds unknown,
   See thee on thy judgment throne,
   Rock of Ages, cleft for me,
   Let me hide myself in thee. Amen.

121

WASHINGTON GLADDEN

February 11, 1836 - July 2, 1918

The many books and articles of this distinguished minister, Washington Gladden, had a great influence for over fifty years and even today his influence lives on through his most loved hymn *O Master, Let Me Walk With Thee.*

Washington Gladden was born in Pottsgrove, Pennsylvania. He graduated from Williams College in 1859 and became a Congregational minister in Brooklyn, New York. In 1882 he moved to the First Congregational Church in Columbus, Ohio, where he remained as pastor for thirty-two years.

Above all, Washington Gladden is remembered for his strong belief that Christians must put their religion to practical daily use and thereby right many social and civil injustices. In one of his last sermons he said, "I have never doubted that the kingdom I have always prayed for is coming, that the gospel I have preached is true . . . that the nation is being saved."

HENRY PERCY SMITH

1825 - 1898

Henry Percy Smith, composer of the music to which we sing *O Master, Let Me Walk With Thee,* was born in England, educated at Oxford and ordained in the Church of England in 1850. He was appointed perpetual Curate of St. Michael's in 1851 and stayed until 1868 when he was appointed Vicar of Great Barton, Suffolk. From 1882 until 1895 he was chaplain at Christ Church, Cannes, France, and beginning in 1892, Canon of the Cathedral at Gibraltar.

O Master, Let Me Walk With Thee

Washington Gladden   *H. Percy Smith*

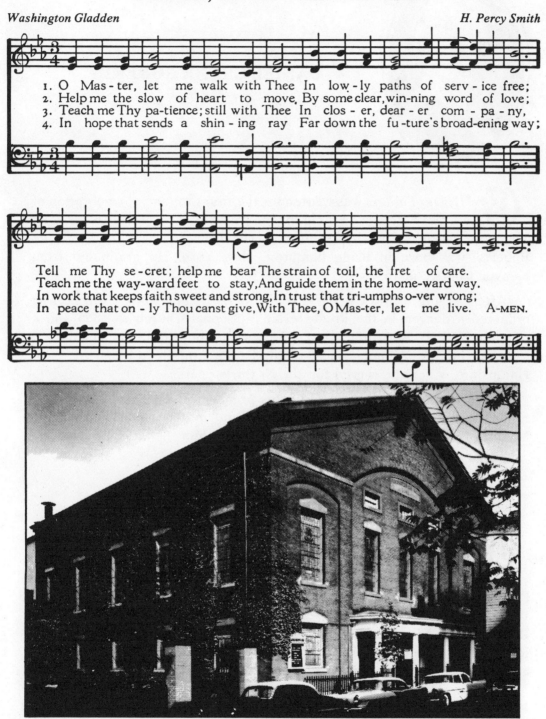

1. O Mas-ter, let me walk with Thee In low-ly paths of serv-ice free;
2. Help me the slow of heart to move, By some clear, win-ning word of love;
3. Teach me Thy pa-tience; still with Thee In clos-er, dear-er com-pa-ny,
4. In hope that sends a shin-ing ray Far down the fu-ture's broad-ening way;

Tell me Thy se-cret; help me bear The strain of toil, the fret of care.
Teach me the way-ward feet to stay, And guide them in the home-ward way.
In work that keeps faith sweet and strong, In trust that tri-umphs o-ver wrong;
In peace that on-ly Thou canst give, With Thee, O Mas-ter, let me live. A-MEN.

Plymouth Church Of The Pilgrims

Plymouth Church (1847) and the Church of the Pilgrims (1844) merged in 1934 to form Plymouth Church of the Pilgrims (Congregational), Brooklyn, New York. It was here that Henry Ward Beecher published the first hymnal to have both words and music on the same page (see page 112). Plymouth Church has been designated a National Historic Landmark.

DANIEL CRANE ROBERTS

November 5, 1841 - October 31, 1907

God Of Our Fathers was written for the first Centennial celebration of the United States and sung for the first time on July 4, 1876 at St. Thomas Episcopal Church, Brandon, Vermont. Its author, Daniel Crane Roberts, was born in Bridgehampton, New York. He graduated from Kenyon College in 1857.

After serving in the Civil War with the 84th Ohio Volunteers he was ordained a deacon in the Presbyterian Episcopal Church in 1865 and a priest in 1866. He served in many different parishes in Massachusetts and Vermont before becoming Vicar of St. Paul's Church in Concord, New Hampshire, where he served for almost thirty years.

Daniel Crane Roberts also served as president of the New Hampshire State Historical Society for several years and in 1885 was honored by Norwich University, when they conferred upon him their D.D. degree.

GEORGE WILLIAM WARREN

August 17, 1828 - March 17, 1902

George W. Warren, composer of the music for *God Of Our Fathers*, was born in Albany, New York and rose to the top of his profession as an organist without benefit of formal training. After graduation from Racine College, he became organist at St. Peter's Episcopal Church (1846 - 1858) and St. Paul's Church (1858 - 1860) in Albany. Warren went to Brooklyn, New York, in 1860 to serve as organist for Holy Trinity Church. He stayed at Trinity until 1870, when he became organist and choirmaster at St. Thomas' Church in New York City. During his twenty years (1870 - 1890) at St. Thomas' he composed anthems, service music and edited, *Warren's Hymns And Tunes As Sung At St. Thomas' Church* (1888).

Feeling that no organist could play as well as George Warren, not a note of music was played at his funeral, even though thousands of people attended.

God Of Our Fathers

Daniel C. Roberts

George W. Warren

1. God of our fa - thers, whose al-might - y hand
2. Thy love di - vine hath led us in the past;
3. From war's a-larms, from dead-ly pes - ti -lence,
4. Re - fresh Thy peo - ple on their toil-some way;

Leads forth in beau - ty all the star - ry band
In this free land by Thee our lot is cast;
Be Thy strong arm our ev - er sure de - fense;
Lead us from night to nev - er - end - ing day;

Of shin - ing worlds in splen - dor through the skies,
Be Thou our Rul - er, Guard - ian, Guide, and Stay,
Thy true re - li - gion in our hearts in - crease,
Fill all our lives with love and grace di - vine,

Our grate - ful songs be - fore Thy throne a - rise.
Thy Word our law, Thy paths our cho - sen way.
Thy boun - teous good - ness nour - ish us in peace.
And glo - ry, laud, and praise be ev - er Thine. A - MEN.

GEORGE MATHESON

March 27, 1842 - August 28, 1906

George Matheson, author of *O Love That Wilt Not Let Me Go,* was born in Glasgow, Scotland, to the son of a wealthy merchant. In spite of very poor eyesight George was an excellent student, graduating from Glasgow University (B.A. 1861, M.A. 1862). Upon graduation he entered the Divinity School of Glasgow University and was ordained in the Presbyterian ministry in 1866, becoming minister of St. Bernard's in Edinburgh later that year. In 1899, after thirty-three years of service at St. Bernard's, George Matheson retired.

During his career, Matheson preached before Queen Victoria, received an honorary D.D. from Edinburgh University (1879) and an LL.D. from Aberdeen University (1902), in recognition of his outstanding preaching ability and authorship of theological studies.

ALBERT LISTER PEACE

January 26, 1844 - March 14, 1912

Born in Huddersfield, England, Albert was a child prodigy, gifted with perfect pitch. When only five years old Albert could identify any note or chord played on the piano. At the age of nine he received his first professional job as organist at Holmfirth Parish Church, Yorkshire. During his early years Albert Peace played organ at many churches. In 1879 he became organist at Glasgow Cathedral where he remained until 1897, when he was chosen to succeed William T. Best at St. George's Hall, Liverpool. He remained at St. George's until his death twelve years later.

During his career many honors were bestowed upon Albert Lister Peace, including the playing of the opening recitals on the organs at
(Continued under hymn on page 127.)

O Love That Wilt Not Let Me Go

George Matheson

A.L. Peace

1. O Love that wilt not let me go, I rest my weary soul in Thee; I give Thee back the life I owe, That in Thine o-cean depths its flow May rich-er, full-er be.

2. O Light that fol-low'st all my way, I yield my flick-'ring torch to Thee; My heart re-stores its bor-rowed ray. That in Thy sun-shine's glow its day May bright-er, fair-er be.

3. O Joy that seek-est me thro' pain, I can-not close my heart to Thee; I trace the rain-bow thro' the rain. And feel the prom-ise is not vain That morn shall tear-less be.

4. O Cross that lift-est up my head, I dare not ask to hide from Thee; I lay in dust life's glo-ry dead, And from the ground there blossoms red Life that shall end-less be.

(Albert Lister Peace's biography continued.)

Canterbury Cathedral in 1886, Victoria Hall, Hanley in 1888 and Newcastle Cathedral in 1891. Peace's organ playing was marked by his distinctive pedal techniques as a result of which some organ builders extended the range of the pedal organ. One knew when Albert Lister Peace was organist by the strongly marked time and thunderous pedaling, often beating out the measure in semistaccato style, like the double bass in the orchestra.

GEORGE JOB ELVEY

March 27, 1816 - December 9, 1893

The music to which we sing *Crown Him With Many Crowns* was written by George Job Elvey. Elvey was born in Canterbury, England in 1816 into a musical family. As a boy he was chorister at Canterbury Cathedral and with his older brother Stephen studied music at the Royal Academy of Music.

In 1835, at the age of nineteen, he began as organist and master of the boys choir at St. George's Chapel and stayed there until he retired in 1882. While at St. George's, Elvey was awarded a B.M. from New College, Oxford in 1838 and a Mus. D. in 1840.

St. George's was the church of the royal family, and therefore Elvey played for the marriages of the Prince of Wales in 1863, the Princess Louise in 1871, the Duke of Albany in 1882 and other royalty, as well as being in charge of the music for other events of state. In 1871 he was knighted for composing the *Festival March* for the wedding of Princess Louise.

George Elvey composed two oratorios, several odes, many anthems, thirty cathedral chants, fifteen double chants, some secular music and several hymn tunes which are exceedingly inspiring. Elvey believed the music for hymns should be as stately, uplifting and inspiring as high cathedral ceilings and the most beautiful stained glass windows and that the music of the Church should, at least, be suggestive of the sublime music of heaven.

MATTHEW BRIDGES

July 14, 1800 - October 6, 1894

Matthew Bridges, the youngest son of John Bridges was born at Malden, England. He was educated in the Church of England and in 1828, published a polemical book against the Roman Catholic Church entitled *The Roman Empire Under Constantine The Great.* Twenty years later he and other friends associated with the Oxford Movement joined the Catholic Church.

In 1847 and 1851, Matthew Bridges published *Hymns Of the Heart* which contained his beautiful hymn *Crown Him With Many Crowns* and in 1852, his second book of hymns, entitled *In The Passion Of Jesus.* Matthew Bridges spent the later years of his life in Canada. His hymns were introduced in America through Henry Ward Beecher's *Plymouth Collection.*

128

Crown Him With Many Crowns

Matthew Bridges   *George J. Elvey*

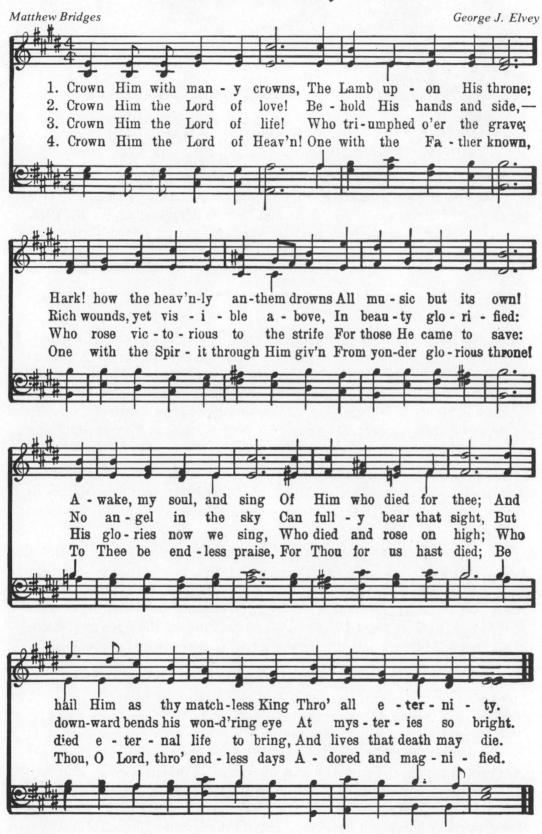

1. Crown Him with man - y crowns, The Lamb up - on His throne;
2. Crown Him the Lord of love! Be - hold His hands and side,—
3. Crown Him the Lord of life! Who tri - umphed o'er the grave;
4. Crown Him the Lord of Heav'n! One with the Fa - ther known,

Hark! how the heav'n-ly an-them drowns All mu - sic but its own!
Rich wounds, yet vis - i - ble a - bove, In beau-ty glo - ri - fied:
Who rose vic - to - rious to the strife For those He came to save:
One with the Spir - it through Him giv'n From yon-der glo - rious throne!

A - wake, my soul, and sing Of Him who died for thee; And
No an - gel in the sky Can full - y bear that sight, But
His glo - ries now we sing, Who died and rose on high; Who
To Thee be end - less praise, For Thou for us hast died; Be

hail Him as thy match-less King Thro' all e - ter - ni - ty.
down-ward bends his won-d'ring eye At mys - ter - ies so bright.
died e - ter - nal life to bring, And lives that death may die.
Thou, O Lord, thro' end - less days A - dored and mag - ni - fied.

EARL BOWMAN MARLATT

May 24, 1892 - June 13, 1976

Earl Marlatt and his twin brother were born in Columbus, Indiana to Mrs. and Reverend Marlatt, a Methodist minister. He was educated at DePauw University (B.A. 1912) and Boston University (S.T.B. 1922, Ph. D. 1929) with further study at Harvard University, Oxford University and the University of Berlin. (During World War I his education was interrupted while he served as second lieutenant in the Field Artillery).

In 1923 he accepted the position as associate professor of philosophy, at Boston University and in 1925 was made full professor.

It was in 1926 that he was asked to write an original hymn for a consecration service at Boston University's Theological Seminary's School of Religious Education, of which he was also a faculty member. Marlatt chose to set his hymn, *Are Ye Able,* to an original tune composed two years earlier by Henry S. Mason, a graduate student at the Seminary. *Are Ye Able* was a great success when sung for the first time at Pilgrim Hall, and as the years passed it increased in popularity.

Earl Marlatt was named dean in 1938 and served until 1945 when he accepted a post at the Perkins School of Theology at Southern Methodist University in Texas. Here he served as professor of the philosophy of religion and religious literature.

During his brilliant career Earl Marlatt wrote several hymns and four books, two of which were poetry. (He was the first to win Boston's coveted May Day Poetry Tournament in 1925.) He was associate editor of *The American Student Hymnal* (1928) and retained a keen interest in hymnology, serving from 1958 to 1962, as curator of the Treasure Room and Hymn Museum at the Interchurch Center in New York City.

HARRY SILVERNALE MASON

October 17, 1881 - November 15, 1964

Harry Silvernale Mason was born in Gloversville, New York and educated at Syracuse University (B.M. 1911), with graduate study at Boston University (1924-1926). From 1916 to 1939 he served as organist of Auburn Theological Seminary and instructor of music (1917-1935) and assistant professor of fine arts and religion (1935-1939). While working at Auburn Theological Seminary, he was also organist of the First Presbyterian Church and later, the Second Presbyterian Church of Auburn, where he served for twenty-seven years.

Are Ye Able

Earl Marlatt   *Harry S. Mason*

1. "Are ye a - ble," said the Mas - ter, "To be cru - ci - fied with me?—"
2. "Are ye a - ble" to re - mem - ber, When a thief lifts up his eyes,
3. "Are ye a - ble" when the shad - ows Close a - round you with the sod,
4. "Are ye a - ble?" Still the Mas - ter Whis - pers down e - ter - ni - ty,

"Yea," the sturd - y dream - ers an - swered, "To the death we fol - low Thee."
That his par - doned soul is wor - thy Of a place in par - a - dise?
To be - lieve that spir - it tri - umphs, To com - mend your soul to God?
And he - ro - ic spir - its an - swer Now, as then, in Gal - i - lee.

REFRAIN

"Lord, we are a - ble." Our spir - its are Thine. Re - mold them,

make us, Like Thee, di - vine. Thy guid - ing ra - diance A - bove us shall

be A bea - con to God, To love and loy - al - ty. A - MEN.

PHILLIPS BROOKS

December 13, 1835 - January 23, 1893

Traveling by horseback from Jerusalem to Bethlehem on December 24, 1865, Phillips Brooks, the pastor of Holy Trinity Episcopal Church in Philadelphia, was deeply moved as he journeyed through the very field where the shepherds saw and heard the angels proclaim Jesus birth. He wrote to his Sunday school children of the experience and two years after his Holy Land visit, at the age of thirty-two, wrote the immortal *O Little Town Of Bethlehem.*

Phillips Brooks was born in Boston, Massachusetts. He was educated at the Boston Latin School, Harvard University and Virginia Theological Seminary. He was ordained an Episcopal priest in 1859. Phillips began his ministry in Philadelphia at the Church of the Advent. Three years later he was named rector of Holy Trinity Church in that city. It was here that he wrote *O Little Town Of Bethlehem* and asked his organist and Sunday school superintendent, Lewis Henry Redner, to write the music.

In 1869 Brooks became rector of the famous Trinity Church in Boston. When fire swept through the heart of Boston in 1871 it destroyed Trinity Church and a new, massive stone church was erected on Copley Square. Here for the next twenty-two years Phillips Brooks became recognized as one of our nation's greatest preachers and many, many volumes of his sermons were published.

Phillips Brooks never married but he had a great love for children and wrote many of his hymns for them. He moved with equal ease among young and old, rich and poor. He preached, by special request, before Queen Victoria and filled such famous places as Westminster Abbey and St. Paul's Cathedral in London.

He delivered the famous *Lectures On Preaching* at Yale Divinity School in 1877 and received the D.D. degree from Oxford University in 1885. In 1891, Phillips Brooks was appointed by the Episcopal Church as Bishop of Massachusetts, a post he filled with distinction until his untimely death, shortly before his fifty-ninth birthday.

O Little Town of Bethlehem

Phillips Brooks   *Lewis H. Redner*

1. O lit-tle town of Beth-le-hem, How still we see thee lie! A - bove thy deep and
2. For Christ is born of Ma - ry, And gathered all a - bove, While mortals sleep, the
3. How si-lent-ly, how si-lent-ly, The wondrous gift is given! So God im-parts to
4. O ho-ly Child of Beth-le-hem! De-scend to us, we pray; Cast out our sin, and

dreamless sleep The si - lent stars go by. Yet in thy dark streets shineth The ev - er-
an-gels keep Their watch of wondering love. O morn-ing stars, to-geth - er Proclaim the
human hearts The blessings of His heaven. No ear may hear His com-ing, But in this
en - ter in; Be born in us to - day. We hear the Christmas an-gels The great glad

last-ing Light; The hopes and fears of all the years Are met in thee to-night.
ho - ly birth! And prais-es sing to God the King, And peace to men on earth.
world of sin, Where meek souls will receive Him still, The dear Christ enters in.
ti - dings tell; O come to us, a - bide with us, Our Lord Em-man-u - el. A-MEN.

LEWIS HENRY REDNER

December 15, 1830 - August 29, 1908

Lewis Redner was born in Philadelphia in 1830 and lived there all his life. At the age of sixteen he entered the real estate business and eventually became owner of his own highly successful real estate firm.

He served as organist at four different churches during his career, the longest being his nineteen years at Holy Trinity, where he not only did a great job as organist, but developed their Sunday school from thirty-six children to over one thousand.

Robert Lowry   **William Bradbury**   **William Doane**

SUNDAY SCHOOL HYMNS

Imagine living one hundred years ago. There was no television, no radio, no stereo and even worse, no automobiles. Social life centered around local activities and church. And, when churches expanded their social programs, the Sunday school and Gospel hymn-writers became the equivalent of todays Beatles, Simon & Garfunkel, the Carpenters and Johnny Cash.

The correct term for most of the popular Sunday school and Gospel hymns is probably "Pietist". Prior to the Pietist Movement (which began in Europe in the 1700's) most hymns centered upon the greatness of God and His relationship to mankind. The Pietists reversed the emphasis declaring the individual's love of God (and Jesus) and their personal, intimate relationship to Him. It was thus that the hymns some people refer to as Gospel songs were born in song collections used extensively in Sunday schools, revival meetings and social gatherings.

In the United States, the idea of Sunday schools was introduced following the Revolutionary War. Because many areas did not have any public schools, Sunday schools were also used to teach reading and writing. In 1824 the American Sunday School Union was founded to promote the spread of Sunday schools and to publish the needed materials.

From the 1830's through the 1890's there was an enormous output of Sunday school hymn books and pamphlets. Three of the major composers were William Bradbury, editor of Sunday school song collections for Biglow and Main, Reverend Robert Lowry, who succeeded Bradbury, and William H. Doane, who collaborated with Lowry on most of his publications. Of course there were many other great writers, but it is the works of these **three men that are still prominent today through their famous hymns.**

Ira Sankey

Dwight Moody

Phillip Bliss

GOSPEL HYMNS

Ira D. Sankey began working with evangelist Dwight L. Moody in 1870 as song leader and soloist. When Moody and Sankey traveled England in 1872 holding revival meetings Sankey developed what later became the best selling hymn book, *Sacred Songs And Solos* (which has sold over eighty million copies and is still on sale in England).

Phillip Paul Bliss, one of the most widely known and best loved musicians of his day, met Moody in 1869 and with Moody's prompting, became song leader for evangelist Major D.W. Whittle in 1874. Also in 1874 John Church & Company published Bliss's fourth book of hymns, this one entitled *Gospel Songs*.

Bliss suggested to Sankey that they merge their materials. They did and named it *Gospel Hymns And Sacred Songs,* when published in 1875. It was so popular it was followed by *Gospel Hymns No. 2* in 1876, *No. 3* in 1878, *No. 4* in 1881, *No. 5* in 1887 and *No. 6* in 1891.

After Phillip Bliss was tragically killed in a train accident in 1876, Ira Sankey was assisted by two associates of evangelist Dwight Moody and Major Whittle, first James McGranahan and after he retired, George C. Stebbins, to produce volumes *No. 3, No. 4, No. 5* and *No. 6* of *Gospel Hymns*.

To be included in an edition of *Gospel Hymns* could make an obscure hymn a favorite once it was sung and known by the millions of people attending the revival meetings of Dwight L. Moody, Major D.W. Whittle and other evangelists.

In a short time, ten million copies of *Gospel Hymns*, each containing about seven hundred hymns, were sold at the bargain price of 35 cents and the term "Gospel Hymn" became a part of our language.

WILLIAM BATCHELDER BRADBURY

October 6, 1816 - January 7, 1868

Of these *One Hundred And One Famous Hymns* the music for five of them was written by the same great tune composer and compiler of Sunday school hymns, William Bradbury.

Bradbury was born at York, Maine. His father, a veteran of the Revolutionary War, was a choir leader. William went to Boston when he was fourteen and lived at the home of Sumner Hill, a musician and teacher. While there, he entered the Boston Academy of Music and joined Lowell Mason's choir at the Bowdoin Street Church. Within a short time he became organist at several small churches in succession, until he reached the Baptist Tabernacle in New York City. Here, he also conducted singing classes much like those of his teacher, the renown Lowell Mason in Boston. (Lowell Mason's biography appears on page 100.)

In 1847, Bradbury took his family to Europe and studied music in Leipzig, Germany. Upon his return to New York he devoted his time to teaching, conducting musical conventions, composing and editing books. In 1854 William, with his brother established the Bradbury Piano Company which later became the Knabe Piano Company

William Bradbury was associated with the publishing of fifty-nine collections of sacred and secular music. He also composed a number of glee books and the *Devotional Hymn And Tune Book* for Baptist churches. Some of Bradbury's most popular music books were: *The Mendelssohn Collection* (1849), *Shawn* (1853), *The Jubilee* (1858) and *The Golden Chain* (1861).

Savior, Like a Shepherd Lead Us

Anonymous   *William B. Bradbury*

1. Sav-ior, like a shep-herd lead us, Much we need Thy ten-der care;
2. We are Thine; do Thou be-friend us, Be the Guardian of our way;
3. Thou hast promised to re-ceive us, Poor and sin-ful though we be;
4. Ear-ly let us seek Thy fa-vor; Ear-ly let us do Thy will;

In Thy pleas-ant pas-tures feed us, For our use Thy folds pre-pare:
Keep Thy flock, from sin de-fend us, Seek us when we go a-stray:
Thou hast mer-cy to re-lieve us, Grace to cleanse, and pow'r to free:
Bless-ed Lord and on-ly Sav-ior, With Thy love our bos-oms fill:

Bless-ed Je-sus, Bless-ed Je-sus, Thou hast bought us, Thine we are;
Bless-ed Je-sus, Bless-ed Je-sus, Hear Thy chil-dren when they pray;
Bless-ed Je-sus, Bless-ed Je-sus, Ear-ly let us turn to Thee;
Bless-ed Je-sus, Bless-ed Je-sus, Thou hast loved us, love us still:

Bless-ed Je-sus, Bless-ed Je-sus, Thou hast bought us, Thine we are.
Bless-ed Je-sus, Bless-ed Je-sus, Hear Thy chil-dren when they pray.
Bless-ed Je-sus, Bless-ed Je-sus, Ear-ly let us turn to Thee.
Bless-ed Je-sus, Bless-ed Je-sus, Thou hast loved us, love us still.

ROBERT LOWRY

March 12, 1826 - November 25, 1899

Robert Lowry, composer of the music to which we sing *I Need Thee Every Hour*, and one of the three big names in Sunday school hymnody, was born in Philadelphia, Pennsylvania, the son of Crozier Lowry who owned the local tavern. He was educated at Bucknell University. From 1854 to 1858 he served pastorates at Westchester, Pennsylvania and from 1859 to 1861 pastorates in New York City. When in 1861, Lowry became pastor of the Hanson Place Baptist Church in Brooklyn, he became intensely interested in writing hymns and tunes.

Succeeding William B. Bradbury in 1868, as editor of Sunday school song collections for Biglow and Main, he produced eight hymn collections, many of which were in collaboration with William H. Doane, including the famous *Gospel Melodies* (1868), *Bright Jewels* (1869) and *Pure Gold* (1871).

In 1869 Robert Lowry left Hanson Place Baptist Church for a pastorate in Lewisburg, Pennsylvania, where he was also professor of belles-lettres at Bucknell University. At this time, he was easily as famous as John Philip Sousa or Irving Berlin were in their day. Receiving his D.D. degree from Bucknell in 1875, Lowry became pastor of the Park Avenue Baptist Church in Plainfield, New Jersey, where he remained for the rest of his life.

The most famous hymn for which Robert Lowry wrote both words and music was *Shall We Gather At The River?* Here's his story of the writing of that wonderful hymn:

"One afternoon in July, 1864, when I was pastor of Hanson Place Baptist Church, Brooklyn, New York, the weather was oppressively hot and I was lying on a lounge in a state of physical exhaustion ... Visions of the future passed before me with startling vividness. The imagery of the Apocalypse took the form of a tableau. Brightest of all were the throne, the heavenly river and the gathering of the saints. My soul seemed to take new life from the celestial outlook. I began to wonder why the hymn-writers had said so much about the river of death, and so little about pure water of life, clear as crystal, proceeding out of the throne of God and of the Lamb. As I mused, the words

(Continued on page 139.)

138

I Need Thee Every Hour

Annie S. Hawks   *Robert Lowry*

1. I need Thee ev-ery hour, Most gra-cious Lord; No ten-der voice like Thine
2. I need Thee ev-ery hour; Stay Thou near by; Temp-ta-tions lose their power
3. I need Thee ev-ery hour, In joy or pain; Come quick-ly and a-bide,
4. I need Thee ev-ery hour; Teach me Thy will; And Thy rich prom-is - es

REFRAIN

Can peace af - ford.   I need Thee, O I need Thee, Ev-ery hour I
When Thou art nigh.
Or life is vain.
In me ful - fill

need Thee; O bless me now, my Sav-iour, I come to Thee!   A - MEN.

(Robert Lowry's biography continued.)

began to construct themselves. They came first as a question of Christian inquiry, --
Shall We Gather? They then broke out in chorus, as an answer of Christian faith -- Yes,
we'll Gather ... the hymn developed itself. The music came with the words."

Few writers of hymns and hymn music were as successful as Robert
Lowry at producing very popular works, but he was totally unconcerned
with success. To Robert Lowry, writing hymns and hymn music was his
very beautiful and enjoyable hobby, to deliver a great sermon was his profession.

The biography of Annie Sherwood Hawks, author of *I Need Thee Every
Hour,* appears on page 140.

FREDERICK WHITFIELD

January 7, 1829 - September 13, 1904

Frederick Whitfield, author of *Oh, How I Love Jesus*, was born in Threapwood, England, and educated at Trinity College Dublin, Ireland. He was ordained in the Church of England in 1859. He became Curate of Otley, Vicar of Kirby-Ravensworth, senior Curate of Greenwich and Vicar of St. John's Bexley. In 1875 he became Vicar of St. Mary's Church, Hastings. During his career he published about thirty volumes of prose and verse.

ANNIE SHERWOOD HAWKS

May 28, 1835 - January 3, 1918

I Need Thee Every Hour (page 139) was first sung at the convention of the National Baptist Sunday School Association at Cincinnati in 1872. Concerning the writing of *I Need Thee Every Hour* Annie Hawks said:

"... when in the midst of the daily cares of my home ... I was so filled with the sense of nearness of the Master that, wondering how one could live without Him, either in joy or pain, these words, 'I need Thee every hour', were ushered into my mind, the thought at once taking full possession of me ... It was not until long years after, when the shadow fell over my way -- the shadow of a great loss -- that I understood something of the comforting in the words I had been permitted to write ..."

Annie Sherwood Hawks was born in Hoosick, New York. In 1859 she married Charles H. Hawks. They lived in Brooklyn, raised three children, and were members of the Hanson Place Baptist Church. It was here that Reverend Robert Lowry discovered her writing talent and in 1868 encouraged Annie Hawks to write hymns. And write she did, producing over four hundred beautiful hymns.

After her husband's death in 1888 Annie Hawks moved to Bennington, Vermont and lived out her life with her daughter and son-in-law, Dr. and Mrs. W.E. Putnam.

Oh, How I Love Jesus

Frederick Whitfield

Traditional Melody

1. There is a name I love to hear, I love to sing its worth; It sounds like
2. It tells me of a Sav-ior's love, Who died to set me free; It tells me
3. It tells me what my Fa-ther hath In store for ev-'ry day, And tho' I
4. It tells of One whose loving heart Can feel my deep-est woe, Who in each

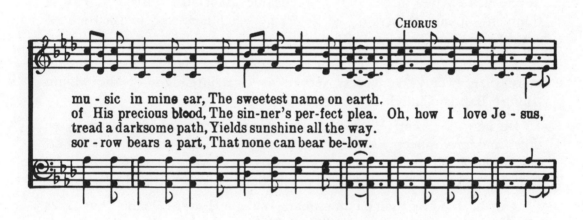

CHORUS

mu-sic in mine ear, The sweetest name on earth.
of His precious blood, The sin-ner's per-fect plea. Oh, how I love Je-sus,
tread a darksome path, Yields sunshine all the way.
sor-row bears a part, That none can bear be-low.

Oh, how I love Je-sus, Oh, how I love Je-sus, Be-cause He first loved me!

WILLIAM HOWARD DOANE

February 3, 1832 - December 24, 1915

Born in Preston, Connecticut, William Doane, inventor and industrialist, was never too busy to write music for a beautiful hymn.

William was educated at Woodstock Academy where at the age of fourteen he directed the school choir. Upon completion of his schooling he went to work for his father's cotton manufacturing business in Norwich, Connecticut. After three years he became associated with J.A. Fay & Company, manufacturers of woodworking machinery and in 1860 moved with the firm to Cincinnati, Ohio.

Doane became a beloved Cincinnati civic and church leader and for more than twenty-five years served as superintendent of the Mount Auburn Baptist Church Sunday school.

During his career, William Doane wrote twenty-two hundred hymn tunes and forty collections. Many of them were in collaboration with Robert Lowry and America's most loved gospel hymn writer, Fanny Crosby who frequently provided hymns for the music Doane composed and sent to her.

A dedicated Christian businessman, William Howard Doane, thus takes his place along with musician William Bradbury and the Reverend Robert Lowry in the development of Sunday school hymns, many of which are today's most loved hymns.

LYDIA ODELL BAXTER

September 8, 1809 - June 22, 1874

Lydia Odell Baxter, author of *Take The Name Of Jesus With You*, was born in Petersburg, New York. After her marriage she moved with her husband to New York City, where following a serious illness she became an invalid. Confined to her bed much of the time, her home became a gathering place for ministers and church workers.

She published a collection of religious poems, *Gems By The Wayside* (1855) and wrote a number of hymns, of which *Take The Name Of Jesus With You*, lives on in the hearts of Christians everywhere.

Take the Name of Jesus with You

Lydia Baxter   *William H. Doane*

1. Take the name of Je-sus with you, Child of sor-row and of woe;
2. Take the name of Je-sus ev-er, As a shield from ev-'ry snare;
3. O the precious name of Je-sus! How it thrills our souls with joy,
4. At the name of Je-sus bow-ing, Fall-ing pros-trate at His feet,

It will joy and com-fort give you, Take it, then, wher-e'er you go.
If temp-ta-tions round you gath-er, Breathe that ho-ly name in prayer.
When His lov-ing arms re-ceive us, And His songs our tongues em-ploy!
King of kings in Heav'n we'll crown Him, When our jour-ney is com-plete.

CHORUS

Pre-cious name,   O how sweet!   Hope of earth and joy of Heav'n;
Precious name,   O how sweet!

Pre-cious name,   O how sweet!... Hope of earth and joy of Heav'n.
Precious name, O how sweet, how sweet!

HORATIO GATES SPAFFORD

October 20, 1828 - October 16, 1888

Horatio Spafford, author of *It Is Well With My Soul*, was born in North Troy, New York and moved to Chicago in 1856. He established a successful legal practice and became professor of medical jurisprudence of Lind University. He was also active in YMCA work and a Sunday school teacher for his Presbyterian Church. In 1870 he visited England and Scotland and became very interested in Bible archaeology. Returning to Chicago, he bought a great deal of real estate on the lake front. Then tragedy struck repeatedly.

First, the Chicago fire of 1871 wiped out his real estate holdings. Then, in 1873, upon the advice of his wife's physician he planned a family vacation in Europe. Spafford sent his family ahead aboard the ship Ville du Havre. Out on the high seas, the Ville du Havre collided with the Lochearn and sunk. Mrs. Spafford was saved but their four daughters perished. Spafford took the next boat to meet his wife in Cardiff, Wales, where the survivors had been taken and while sailing past the spot where his daughters perished, wrote *It Is Well With My Soul*. After their son also died an untimely death in 1880 the Spafford's decided to pursue their interests in the Holy Land and with a group of friends, left Chicago to establish the American Colony in Jerusalem in 1881.

While in Chicago, Horatio G. Spafford was a close friend of evangelist Dwight L. Moody, Ira Sankey and Philip Bliss who upon hearing of the tragedy wrote the music to Spafford's poem, *It Is Well With My Soul*. The biography of composer Philip Paul Bliss appears on page 146.

Today Horatio Spafford's grand-daughter Mrs. Anna Grace Vester Lind, is head of the Spafford Children's Center in Jerusalem carrying on the charitable enterprise begun by her grandparents when they founded Spafford Children's Hospital.

It Is Well With My Soul

H. G. Spafford

P. P. Bliss

1. When peace, like a riv-er, at-tend-eth my way, When sor-rows like
2. Though Sa-tan should buf-fet, tho' tri-als should come, Let this blest as-
3. My sin—oh, the bliss of this glo-ri-ous tho't—My sin—not in
4. And, Lord, haste the day when the faith shall be sight, The clouds be rolled

sea-bil-lows roll; What-ev-er my lot, Thou hast taught me to say,
sur-ance con-trol, That Christ has re-gard-ed my help-less es-tate,
part, but the whole, Is nailed to the cross and I bear it no more,
back as a scroll, The trump shall re-sound and the Lord shall de-scend,

CHORUS

It is well, it is well with my soul.
And hath shed His own blood for my soul. It is well . . . . . with my
Praise the Lord, praise the Lord, O my soul!
"E-ven so"—it is well with my soul. It is well

soul, ... It is well, it is well with my soul.
with my soul,

PHILIP PAUL BLISS

July 9, 1838 - December 29, 1876

Philip P. Bliss, composer of *It Is Well With My Soul* **(page 145)**, was born in a log cabin at Clearfield County, Pennsylvania. At the age of eleven he left home to work on farms and in lumber camps. When Philip attended a music convention in Rome, Pennsylvania, conducted by William B. Bradbury, it proved to be the start of a new way of life. He married Lucy Young in 1859 and worked on his father-in-law's farm. The following year, with his horse Old Fanny and a twenty-dollar melodeon, Philip began his professional music career teaching singing schools during the winter months.

In 1864 he sold his first song to Root and Cady Company and went to work for them, writing and traveling to promote songs until 1868 (can you imagine being a song promoter before there was radio or television?). Through his travels promoting songs, Philip became a widely known song leader, soloist, teacher and music writer. When Philip became Sunday school superintendent and choir director of Chicago's First Congregational Church he met evangelist Dwight L. Moody and with his persistent encouragement, Bliss became a singing evangelist and song leader with evangelist Major D. W. Whittle in March of 1874.

In December of 1876 the Bliss family went to visit his family in Rome, Pennsylvania. After Christmas, Philip and his wife Lucy left their children in Rome and took a train to Chicago to rejoin Major Whittle for a combined New Year's Eve engagement with Whittle and Moody at the Moody Tabernacle. As the train crossed a ravine near Ashtabula, Ohio, the bridge gave way and seven cars plunged seventy feet into the river bed below. Philip escaped through a window but when his wife failed to follow him out, he went back into the wreckage. It burst into flames and they both perished.

When in 1874 Philip Bliss compiled a small collection of hymns for John Church and Company (see page 135), he coined a term that would live on forever when he named it *Gospel Songs.*

Were You There?

Anonymous

Spiritual

1 Were you there when they cru-ci-fied my Lord? Were you
2 Were you there when they nailed him to the tree? Were you
3 Were you there when they laid him in the tomb? Were you

there when they cru-ci-fied my Lord?
there when they nailed him to the tree? Oh!
there when they laid him in the tomb?

Some-times it caus-es me to trem-ble, trem-ble, trem-ble.

Were you there when they cru-ci-fied my Lord?
Were you there when they nailed him to the tree?
Were you there when they laid him in the tomb?

4 Were you there when he rose from the dead?
5 Were you there when he ascended on high?

147

DANIEL WEBSTER WHITTLE

November 22, 1840 - March 4, 1901

Daniel Webster Whittle, author of *There Shall Be Showers Of Blessing,* was born in Chicopee Falls, Massachusetts and during his youth moved to Chicago where he worked for the Wells Fargo Bank. He joined the 72nd Illinois Infantry in 1861 and rose to provost marshal on the staff of General O. O. Howard. While marching to the sea with the troops of General Sherman he was wounded at Vicksburg. Daniel Whittle was promoted to major at the close of the Civil War and was known by this title the rest of his life.

Upon return to Chicago, Whittle became treasurer of Elgin Watch Company. Being very active in church work, Whittle worked with Philip Bliss in several Sunday school conventions.

From Scotland, where Dwight L. Moody was holding revival meetings with Ira Sankey, Moody wrote Whittle and Bliss saying, ''Launch out into the deep . . . If you have not faith of your own in this matter, start out on my faith ''.

At Moody's prompting, Whittle and Bliss agreed to conduct a trial campaign, March 24-26, 1874, at the First Congregational Church of Waukegan, Illinois. Whittle's preaching and Bliss's music met with great success and as a result Major Whittle resigned his lucrative job with Elgin Watch even though they offered to double his salary to become a full time evangelist.

Major Whittle was very successful and with the successive assistance of three outstanding song leaders, Philip Bliss, James McGranahan and George Stebbins, he conducted inspiring revival meetings throughout the United States and twice visited England and Ireland.

Major Whittle wrote two hundred hymns, many of them under the pseudonym ''El Nathan'' which means ''God Has Given'', because he felt it was God and not he writing them. His hymn *There Shall Be Showers Of Blessing* was the first published in *Gospel Hymns No. 4* in 1883 and has been popular ever since.

The biography of James McGranahan, composer of the music to which we sing *There Shall Be Showers Of Blessing* **appears on page 150.**

There Shall Be Showers of Blessing

El Nathan
[*D. W. Whittle*]

James McGranahan

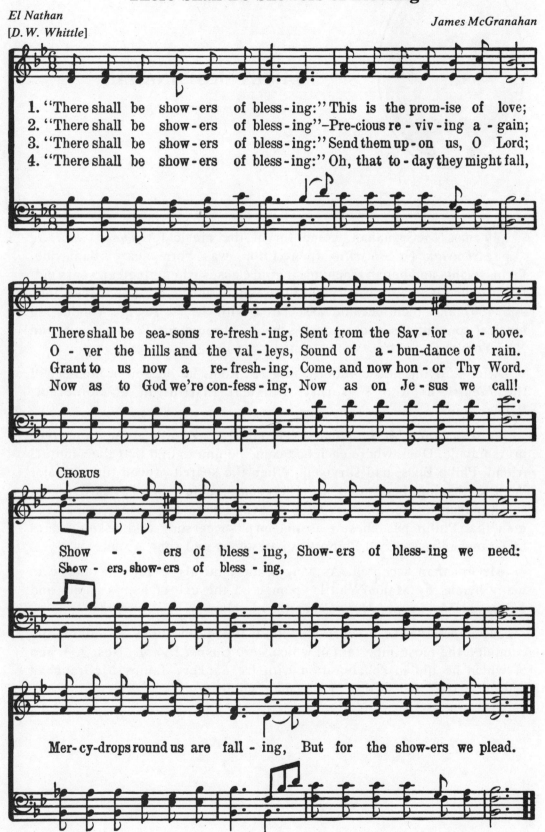

1. "There shall be show-ers of bless-ing:" This is the prom-ise of love;
2. "There shall be show-ers of bless-ing"–Pre-cious re-viv-ing a-gain;
3. "There shall be show-ers of bless-ing:" Send them up-on us, O Lord;
4. "There shall be show-ers of bless-ing:" Oh, that to-day they might fall,

There shall be sea-sons re-fresh-ing, Sent from the Sav-ior a-bove.
O-ver the hills and the val-leys, Sound of a-bun-dance of rain.
Grant to us now a re-fresh-ing, Come, and now hon-or Thy Word.
Now as to God we're con-fess-ing, Now as on Je-sus we call!

CHORUS

Show - - - ers of bless-ing, Show-ers of bless-ing we need:
Show - ers, show-ers of bless-ing,

Mer-cy-drops round us are fall-ing, But for the show-ers we plead.

JAMES McGRANAHAN

July 4, 1840 - July 7, 1907

𝕵ames McGranahan, composer of the music for *There Shall Be Showers Of Blessing* **(page 149)**, was born near Adamsville, Pennsylvania and began teaching singing classes when nineteen years old. He attended Bradbury's Normal Music School during the summer of 1861 and 1862 and then became associated with J. G. Towner conducting musical conventions and singing schools throughout Pennsylvania and New York until 1864.

After studying music under George F. Root, he became a member of the faculty at Root's Normal Musical Institution at Somerset, Pennsylvania.

In 1876 James McGranahan met Major D.W. Whittle at the train wreck in Ashtabule, Ohio, where each had come hoping to find that their mutual friend, Philip Bliss, had survived. When the search proved futile, Major Whittle (having been told by Bliss only a few weeks earlier that McGranahan wanted to work with an evangelist), felt "Here stands the man that Philip has chosen as his own successor" and asked James McGranahan to succeed Philip Bliss as soloist and song leader.

McGranahan accepted. As song leader, he also wrote the music to many hymns by Major Whittle, pioneered the use of men's choirs and published *The Gospel Male Choir* in two volumes, 1878 and 1883.

McGranahan was associated with many publications as editor and compiler, the most important of which were *Gospel Hymns*, Nos. 3, 4, and 5, which he did in collaboration with Ira Sankey. James McGranahan retired in 1887 and settled in Kinsman, Ohio.

We Gather Together

Anonymous

Netherland Folk Song

1. We gath-er to-geth-er to ask the Lord's bless-ing;
2. Be-side us to guide us, our God with us join-ing,
3. We all do ex-tol Thee, Thou Lead-er tri-um-phant,

He chas-tens and has-tens His will to make known;
Or-dain-ing, main-tain-ing His king-dom di-vine;
And pray that Thou still our De-fend-er wilt be.

The wick-ed op-press-ing now cease from dis-tress-ing,
So from the be-gin-ning the fight we were win-ning:
Let Thy con-gre-ga-tion es-cape trib-u-la-tion:

Sing prais-es to His Name: He for-gets not His own.
Thou, Lord, wast at our side, all glo-ry be Thine!
Thy Name be ev-er praised! O Lord, make us free! A-MEN.

GEORGE COLES STEBBINS

February 26, 1846 - October 6, 1945

George Stebbins, composer of the music for *Take Time To Be Holy*, was a descendant of Rowland Stebbins who came to Springfield, Massachusetts in 1634. Born at East Carlton, New York, George helped his dad on the farm and attended the local country school At the age of thirteen he enrolled in a singing school and liked it so much he decided to become a professional musician. In 1868 he moved to Chicago, married and became a clerk at Lyon & Healy music store.

In 1869 Stebbins became director of music at Chicago's First Baptist Church and also song leader for evangelist Reverend Dr. Pentecost.

In the wake of the great Chicago fire (which destroyed his church) George returned to Boston. He became a song leader at Dr. A. J. Gordon's Church and in 1876 director of music at Tremont Temple. It was here that George Stebbins met evangelist Dwight L. Moody who persuaded him to enter evangelistic work on a full-time basis.

For the next twenty-three years George was associated with Moody, while working as song leader for evangelist Major D. W. Whittle. George Stebbins not only followed James McGranahan as song leader with Major Whittle he also worked with Moody's song leader Ira Sankey to compile volumes Nos. 5 and 6 of *Gospel Songs,* the famous hymnal of the evangelists. George Stebbins, the gospel singing evangelist, died at Catskill, New York at ninety-nine years of age.

WILLIAM DUNN LONGSTAFF

January 28, 1822 - April 2, 1894

The most loved hymn, *Take Time To Be Holy,* is the only hymn known to be written by this dedicated layman, William Dunn Longstaff, who was born in Sunderland, England, the son of a wealthy ship owner. When Longstaff's friend, Reverend Arthur A. Rees, left the Church of England to establish the Bethesda Free Chapel, Longstaff provided the money for the needed alterations and served as treasurer.

Among Longstaff's close American friends were Dwight L. Moody, Ira Sankey, D.W. Whittle, George Stebbins and William Booth of the Salvation Army. They not only stayed at his home when in England but also preached at Bethesda Free Chapel.

Take Time To Be Holy

William D. Longstaff   *George C. Stebbins*

1. Take time to be ho - ly, Speak oft with thy Lord;
2. Take time to be ho - ly, The world rush - es on;
3. Take time to be ho - ly, Let Him be thy Guide,
4. Take time to be ho - ly, Be calm in thy soul,

A - bide in Him al - ways, And feed on His Word;
Spend much time in se - cret With Je - sus a - lone;
And run not be - fore Him, What - ev - er be - tide;
Each thought and each mo - tive Be - neath His con - trol;

Make friends of God's chil - dren, Help those who are weak,
By look - ing to Je - sus, Like Him thou shalt be;
In joy or in sor - row, Still fol - low the Lord,
Thus led by His Spir - it To foun - tains of love,

For - get - ting in noth - ing His bless - ing to seek.
Thy friends in thy con - duct His like - ness shall see.
And, look - ing to Je - sus, Still trust in His Word.
Thou soon shalt be fit - ted For serv - ice a - bove.

A - MEN.

DANIEL BRINK TOWNER
March 5, 1850 - October 3, 1919

Daniel B. Towner was born in Rome, Pennsylvania, and received his early musical training from his father, the well known professor J.G. Towner.

From 1870 to 1882 Daniel served as music director of the Centenary Methodist Episcopal Church in Binghamton, New York. Then he went to the York Street Methodist Episcopal Church in Cincinnati for two years and from there to the Union Methodist Episcopal Church in Covington, Kentucky. In 1885 evangelist Dwight L. Moody convinced Daniel Towner to join him on the "saw-dust trail". Daniel Towner became well known for his beautiful baritone voice and great skill as choral conductor.

It was while touring Massachusetts that Towner wrote *Trust And Obey:* "Mr. Moody was conducting a series of meetings in Brockton, Massachusetts, and I had the pleasure of singing for him there. One night a young man rose in a testimony meeting and said, 'I am not quite sure -- but I am going to trust, and I'm going to obey.' I just jotted that sentence down, and sent it with the little story to the Reverend J.H. Sammis, a Presbyterian minister. He wrote the hymn, and the tune was born. The chorus was written before the hymn was."

In 1890 Moody founded the Moody Bible Institute in Chicago to train evangelists and "give great prominence to the study of music". Three years later he named Daniel Towner head of the music department. More than two thousand hymns have been credited to Daniel Towner and he was associated with the publication of fourteen collections.

Daniel Towner died as he lived, while leading the music in an evangelistic meeting in Longwood, Missouri.

JOHN H. SAMMIS
July 6, 1846 - June 12, 1919

John Sammis was born in Brooklyn, New York and at the age of twenty-three moved to Logansport, Indiana. He decided to enter the ministry and upon graduation from Lane Theological Seminary in 1881, was ordained a Presbyterian minister.

John Sammis served pastorates in Iowa, Indiana, Michigan and Minnesota, after which he joined the faculty of the Los Angeles Bible Institute.

Trust and Obey

John H. Sammis   *Daniel B. Towner*

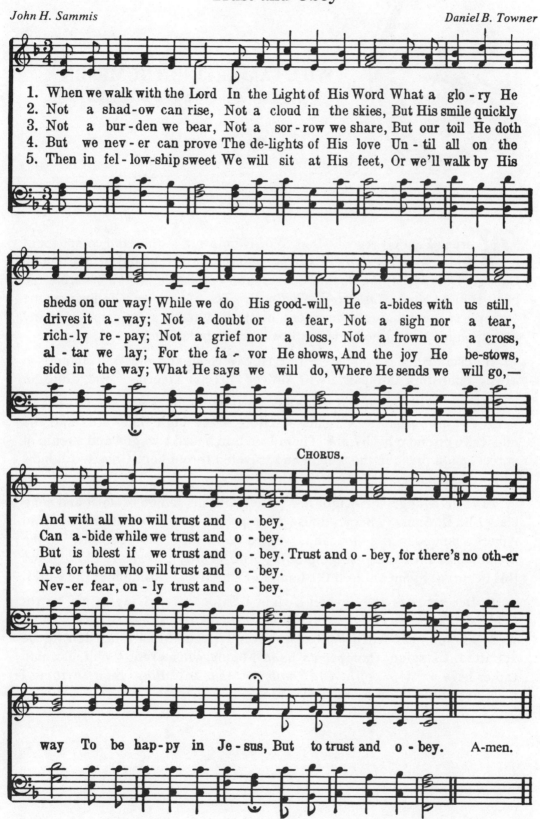

1. When we walk with the Lord In the Light of His Word What a glo-ry He
2. Not a shad-ow can rise, Not a cloud in the skies, But His smile quickly
3. Not a bur-den we bear, Not a sor-row we share, But our toil He doth
4. But we nev-er can prove The de-lights of His love Un-til all on the
5. Then in fel-low-ship sweet We will sit at His feet, Or we'll walk by His

sheds on our way! While we do His good-will, He a-bides with us still,
drives it a-way; Not a doubt or a fear, Not a sigh nor a tear,
rich-ly re-pay; Not a grief nor a loss, Not a frown or a cross,
al-tar we lay; For the fa-vor He shows, And the joy He be-stows,
side in the way; What He says we will do, Where He sends we will go,—

CHORUS.

And with all who will trust and o-bey.
Can a-bide while we trust and o-bey.
But is blest if we trust and o-bey. Trust and o-bey, for there's no oth-er
Are for them who will trust and o-bey.
Nev-er fear, on-ly trust and o-bey.

way To be hap-py in Je-sus, But to trust and o-bey. A-men.

WILL LAMARTINE THOMPSON

November 7, 1847 - September 20, 1909

orn in East Liverpool, Ohio, Will Thompson, author and composer of *Softly And Tenderly Jesus Is Calling*, was educated at Mt. Union College, Ohio and at the Boston Conservatory of Music, where he wrote the best selling song *Gathering Shells By The Seashore*. Following the example of several great composers he studied music at Leipzig, Germany and upon his return home wrote two more popular songs.

He established a book store in East Liverpool and the Will Thompson Music Publishng Company, with offices in East Liverpool and Chicago.

In 1840 Will Thompson wrote his greatest hymn *Softly And Tenderly Jesus Is Calling* and as was his practice, wrote both the words and the music. To promote his hymns Thompson purchased a wagon and a team of horses, put a piano in the wagon and traveled throughout Ohio and Illinois singing hymns.

In 1870 evangelist Dwight L. Moody, with his famous soloist and song leader Ira D. Sankey, began to use Thompson's hymn. In both Europe and America people by the thousands walked down the ''saw-dust trail'' to the invitation of Ira Sankey singing *Softly And Tenderly Jesus Is Calling* and this beautiful hymn entered the hearts of Christians throughout the world.

In December of 1899, when Dwight L. Moody lay dying at his Northfield, Massachusetts home, doctors had issued strict orders that no visitors were allowed but when Will Thompson arrived Moody insisted he be admitted. Clasping Thompson's hand Moody whispered, ''Will, I would rather have written '*Softly And Tenderly Jesus Is Calling*' than anything I have been able to do in my whole life''.

Softly and Tenderly Jesus Is Calling

Will L. Thompson   *Will L. Thompson*

1. Soft - ly and ten-der-ly Je-sus is call-ing, Call-ing for you and for me;
2. Why should we tarry when Je-sus is pleading, Pleading for you and for me?
3. Time is now fleeting, the moments are passing, Passing from you and from me;
4. Oh, for the won-der-ful love He has promised, Promised for you and for me!

See, on the portals He's waiting and watching, Watching for you and for me.
Why should we linger and heed not His mercies, Mercies for you and for me?
Shadows are gath-er-ing, death-beds are coming, Coming for you and for me.
Though we have sinned, He has mercy and par-don, Par-don for you and for me.

CHORUS *m*   *cresc.*

Come home,.... come home,.... Ye who are wea-ry, come home;....
Come home,   come home,

pp   *ppp*   *rit*   *pp*

Ear-nest-ly, ten-der-ly, Je-sus is call-ing, Call-ing, O sin-ner, come home!

157

EDWIN OTHELLO EXCELL

December 13, 1851 - June 10, 1921

After Edwin Excell wrote his catchy tune for Johnson Oatman's poem, *Count Your Blessings,* it became a favorite of evangelists everywhere.

Edwin Excell was born in Stark County, Ohio, the son of a German Reformed Church minister. As a young man he worked as a bricklayer and plasterer, conducting singing schools in his spare time.

After studying music under George and Frederick Root he moved to Chicago and in 1883 began publishing Gospel hymn books which became very popular. He composed over two thousand hymns, published fifty hymn books and collaborated on another thirty-eight compilations.

For twenty years Excell led the singing for evangelist Sam P. Jones, as well as being active in Sunday school work and leading the singing at their conventions. Edwin Excell died as he lived, leading the singing at Gypsy Smith's revival meeting in Louisville, Kentucky.

Count Your Blessings

Johnson Oatman, Jr.   *Edwin O. Excell*

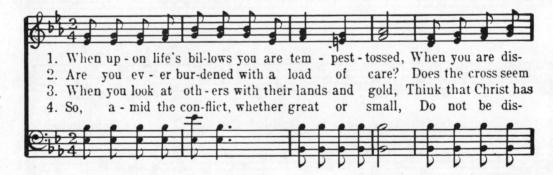

1. When up-on life's bil-lows you are tem - pest-tossed, When you are dis-
2. Are you ev - er bur-dened with a load of care? Does the cross seem
3. When you look at oth - ers with their lands and gold, Think that Christ has
4. So, a - mid the con-flict, whether great or small, Do not be dis-

Count Your Blessings [continued]

cour-aged, think-ing all is lost, Count your man-y bless-ings, name them
heav-y you are called to bear? Count your man-y bless-ings, ev-'ry
prom-ised you His wealth un - told; Count your man-y bless-ings, mon-ey
cour-aged, God is o - ver all; Count your man-y bless-ings, an-gels

one by one, And it will sur-prise you what the Lord hath done.
doubt will fly, And you will be sing-ing as the days go by.
can - not buy Your re-ward in heav-en, nor your home on high.
will at - tend, Help and com-fort give you to your jour - ney's end.

CHORUS.

Count your bless-ings, Name them one by one; Count your
Count your man-y bless-ings, Name them one by one; Count your man-y

bless-ings, See what God hath done; Count your bless-ings,
bless-ings, See what God hath done; Count your man-y bless-ings,

rit.   *a tempo*

Name them one by one; Count your man-y blessings, See what God hath done.

CECIL FRANCIS
HUMPHREYS ALEXANDER

1823 - October 12, 1895

ecil Alexander, author of *Jesus Calls Us,* was the most famous woman writer in all Europe in the field of verse for children. Her *Hymns For Little Children* first published in 1848, passed through sixty-nine editions before the close of the century.

Cecil was born at Miltown House in Tyrone County, Ireland, in 1818. She was the daughter of Major John Humphreys of the Royal Marines, a land-owner and government agent in County Tyrone.

In 1850 Cecil married Reverend William Alexander, rector of the parish of Termonmongan. The gifted bride proved to be the perfect match for her brilliant husband who, in 1867, was appointed Bishop of Derry and Raphoe and in 1896, Archbishop of Armagh and Primate of all Ireland.

During her long career, Cecil devoted much of her time to the unfortunate, especially to the institution named ''The Home for Fallen Women''. Although she wrote over four hundred hymns, her greatest literary work was the poem entitled *The Burial Of Moses.*

WILLIAM HERBERT JUDE

September, 1851 - August 7, 1922

orn at Westleton, England, William Jude, composer of the music to which we sing *Jesus Calls Us,* began his career playing organ at the Blue Coat Hospital in Liverpool. In 1889 he became organist at Stretford Town Hall near Manchester. Later in his career Jude stimulated interest in church music by lecturing. Jude also promoted church music through his editing of the journal *Monthly Hymnal.* Other writings of Jude include *Music And The Higher Life* (1904), *Mission Hymns* (1911) and *Festival Hymns* (1916).

Jesus Calls Us

Mrs. Cecil F. Alexander　　　　　　　　　　　　　　　　*William H. Jude*

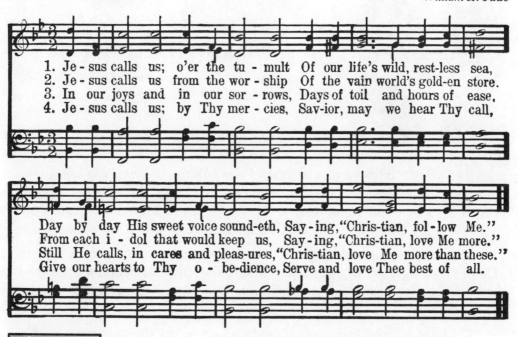

1. Je - sus calls us; o'er the tu - mult Of our life's wild, rest-less sea,
2. Je - sus calls us from the wor - ship Of the vain world's gold-en store.
3. In our joys and in our sor - rows, Days of toil and hours of ease,
4. Je - sus calls us; by Thy mer - cies, Sav-ior, may we hear Thy call,

Day by day His sweet voice sound-eth, Say-ing, "Chris-tian, fol-low Me."
From each i - dol that would keep us, Say-ing, "Chris-tian, love Me more."
Still He calls, in cares and pleas-ures, "Chris-tian, love Me more than these."
Give our hearts to Thy o - be-dience, Serve and love Thee best of all.

THE OLD NORTH CHURCH
Boston, Massachusetts
Immortalized In Longfellow's
"Paul Revere's Ride"

North Church was chartered by the Church of England in 1723, its congregation having out-grown Kings Chapel. The family box pews were designed to hold the heat from coal burning foot warmers and are nearly five feet high. After the Revolutionary War its name was changed to Christ Church, when it affiliated itself with the newly organized Episcopal Church.

CHARLOTTE ELLIOTT

March 18, 1789 - September 22, 1871

harlotte Elliott wrote *Just As I Am, Without One Plea* one night in 1834 while her brother Reverend Henry Elliott, an Anglican minister, and other members of the family were attending church at St. Mary's Hall, Brighton, and she, an invalid, was left home alone.

Charlotte, the granddaughter of the Reverend Henry Venn was born at Clapham, England. In 1821 she fell seriously ill and remained an invalid until she passed away fifty years later. Describing her physical condition she wrote:

> "My Heavenly Father knows, and He alone, what it is, day after day, and hour after hour, to fight against bodily feelings of almost overpowering weakness and languor and exhaustion, to resolve, as He enables me to do, not to yield to the slothfulness, the depression, the irritability, such a body causes me to long to indulge, but to rise every morning determined on taking this for my motto, 'If any man will come after me, let him deny himself, take up his cross daily, and follow me' ".

Charlotte Elliott did not allow her sick body to stop the activity of her keen mind. From 1835 to 1869 she wrote four books of hymns and assisted in the compilation of *The Invalid's Hymn Book* (1834) which contained one hundred and twelve of her one hundred and fifty beautiful hymns.

WILLIAM BATCHELDER BRADBURY

October 6, 1816 - January 7, 1868

The biography of William B. Bradbury, composer of the music to which we sing *Just As I Am, Without One Plea*, appears on page 136.

Just As I Am

Charlotte Elliott

William B. Bradbury

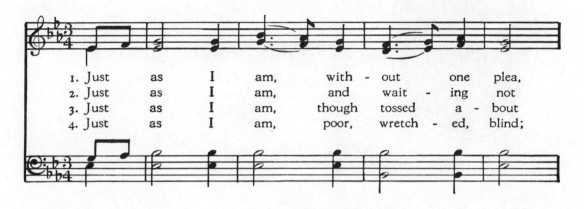

1. Just as I am, with-out one plea,
2. Just as I am, and wait-ing not
3. Just as I am, though tossed a-bout
4. Just as I am, poor, wretch-ed, blind;

But that Thy blood was shed for me, And that Thou bidd'st me
To rid my soul of one dark blot, To Thee whose blood can
With many a con-flict, many a doubt, Fight-ings and fears with-
Sight, rich-es, heal-ing of the mind— Yea, all I need, in

come to Thee, O Lamb of God, I come, I come!
cleanse each spot, O Lamb of God, I come, I come!
in, with-out, O Lamb of God, I come, I come!
Thee to find, O Lamb of God, I come, I come! A-men.

5 Just as I am! Thou wilt receive,
   Wilt welcome, pardon, cleanse, relieve;
   Because Thy promise I believe,
   O Lamb of God, I come!

6 Just as I am! Thy love unknown
   Hath broken every barrier down;
   Now, to be Thine, yea, Thine alone,
   O Lamb of God, I come!

FRANCIS HAROLD ROWLEY

July 25, 1854 - February 14, 1952

Born in Hilton, New York, the son of a physician, Francis Rowley, author of *I Will Sing The Wondrous Story,* was educated at the University of Rochester receiving his B.D. from Rochester Theological Seminary in 1878. Ordained to the Baptist ministry he served churches in Titusville, Pennsylvania, North Adams, Massachusetts, Oak Park, Illinois, Fall River, Massachusetts and the First Baptist Church of Boston.

Regarding his writing of *I Will Sing The Wondrous Story* Reverend Rowley wrote:

"We were having a revival at the First Baptist Church at North Adams, Massachusetts, in 1886, the third year of my pastorate there ... I was assisted by a young Swiss musician named Peter Bilhorn who suggested that I write a hymn for which he would compose the music. The following night the hymn came to me without any particular effort on my part." *

Because of his great love for animals he was elected president of the Massachusetts Society for the Prevention of Cruelty to Animals which also operates an animal hospital in Boston. Rowley served with distinction until 1945, when at the age of ninety-one he was named chairman of the Board of Directors.

The Rowley School of Humanities at Oglethorpe University, Atlanta, Georgia, was named in his honor.

The biography of Peter Philip Bilhorn, composer of *I Will Sing The Wondrous Story,* appears on page 166.

* Alterations in stanzas 2, 3, and 4 were apparently made by Ira Sankey without the author's knowledge when he published it in Gospel Hymns #5 (1887).

I Will Sing the Wondrous Story

PETER PHILIP BILHORN

July 22, 1865 - December 13, 1936

Peter Bilhorn, composer of the music for *I Will Sing The Wondrous Story*, was born in Mendota, Illinois. His family came to America from Bavaria and had their name, Pulhorn, changed to Bilhorn by Abraham Lincoln when Lincoln was a judge in Ottawa, Illinois. Peter barely knew his father George, who was a carriage maker, as his father died shortly after returning from service in the Civil War. In 1876, when Peter was sixteen years old, the family moved to Chicago and later he and his brother, following in their father's footsteps, established the Eureka Wagon and Carriage Works.

Although business was good, Peter loved to sing and became a popular singer in Chicago's German beer gardens.

In 1883 Peter attended a series of revival meetings held by George F. Pentecost and George C. Stebbins and decided to devote himself to religious music. After studying music with Root and Stebbins he traveled extensively with evangelist D.D. O'Dell, George F. Pentecost and John Currie.

When in 1886, Peter accepted an invitation to conduct the music for a series of services being held at the First Baptist Church of North Adams, Massachusetts, he persuaded its minister, Reverend Francis Rowley to write his hymn *I Will Sing The Wondrous Story*.

Peter Bilhorn achieved widespread fame as soloist and song leader. Knowing first-hand the need of evangelists for a small portable organ Peter invented a reed organ which weighed less than fifty pounds and established the Bilhorn Folding Organ Company, Chicago, to manufacture it. It was an immediate success and quickly became a favorite instrument for evangelistic work.

In 1900, Peter Bilhorn conducted a four thousand voice choir in London's Crystal Palace and at the invitation of Queen Victoria sang several of his hymns in the chapel of Buckingham Palace. Prior to 1908, Peter was song leader for evangelist Billy Sunday. As composer and hymn writer, Peter Bilhorn produced over two thousand hymns and his publishing company met with great success.

Just A Closer Walk with Thee

Unknown

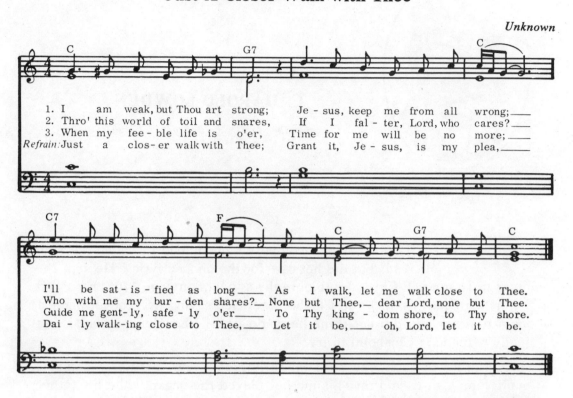

1. I am weak, but Thou art strong; Je-sus, keep me from all wrong;___
2. Thro' this world of toil and snares, If I fal-ter, Lord, who cares?___
3. When my fee-ble life is o'er, Time for me will be no more;___
Refrain: Just a clos-er walk with Thee; Grant it, Je-sus, is my plea,___

I'll be sat-is-fied as long___ As I walk, let me walk close to Thee.
Who with me my bur-den shares?___ None but Thee,___ dear Lord, none but Thee.
Guide me gent-ly, safe-ly o'er___ To Thy king-dom shore, to Thy shore.
Dai-ly walk-ing close to Thee,___ Let it be,___ oh, Lord, let it be.

The First Baptist Church In America Providence, Rhode Island

In 1638, Roger Williams and his companions founded The First Baptist Church in America and in 1775 the above Meeting House was erected. As stated in their bulletin, soul liberty was and continues to be its watchword.

C. HAROLD LOWDEN

October 12, 1883 - February 27, 1963

In 1915 C. Harold Lowden composed the music to which we sing *Living For Jesus* but did not care for the chosen lyrics. He sent the music to Thomas O. Chisholm (biography appears on page 170) and asked that he write new words for it. Chisholm refused saying he, "never made a poem to order and did not think he could do it." Lowden persisted and finally persuaded Chisholm to try.

C. Harold Lowden was born in Burlington, New Jersey, to a music loving family. It is said that his mother played the organ while his father played the trumpet and rocked the cradle with his foot. This may be an exaggeration but it is known that Harold took lessons on a small violin when only five years old. At the age of twelve he sold his first composition to Hall-Mack Company and by the time he was thirteen he conducted the church orchestra.

With schooling completed Harold went to work for Hall-Mack Company. Five years later he became associated with another publisher, John J. Hood, a job he eventually relinquished in 1913 to accept the newly created post of music editor for the Reformed Church in America. After twelve years as music editor he quit to enter business for himself in Camden, New Jersey.

Initially, the business was very successful, then in the financial crash of 1929 the savings of many years were wiped out overnight. Undaunted, Harold carried on, teaching music for eight years at the Bible Institute of Pennsylvania and also, from 1933 on, serving as minister of music at the Linden Baptist Church of Camden, New Jersey. In 1961 he retired ending sixty years of continuous service as choir director and church organist.

The biography of the author, Thomas Chisholm is on page 170.

168

Living for Jesus

Thomas O. Chisholm

C. Harold Lowden

1. Liv-ing for Je-sus a life that is true, Striv-ing to please Him in
2. Liv-ing for Je-sus who died in my place, Bear-ing on Cal-vary my
3. Liv-ing for Je-sus wher-ev-er I am, Do-ing each du-ty in
4. Liv-ing for Je-sus through earth's lit-tle while, My dear-est treas-ure, the

all that I do; Yield-ing al-le-giance, glad-heart-ed and free,
sin and dis-grace; Such love con-strains me to an-swer His call,
His ho-ly name; Will-ing to suf-fer af-flic-tion and loss,
light of His smile; Seek-ing the lost ones He died to re-deem,

Chorus. Unison. Slower

This is the path-way of bless-ing for me.
Fol-low His lead-ing and give Him my all. O Je-sus, Lord and
Deem-ing each tri-al a part of my cross.
Bring-ing the wea-ry to find rest in Him.

Sav-iour, I give my-self to Thee, For Thou, in Thy a-tone-ment, Didst

give Thy-self for me; I own no oth-er Mas-ter, My heart shall be Thy

throne.   My life I give, henceforth to live, O Christ, for Thee a - lone.

THOMAS OBEDIAH CHISHOLM

July 29, 1866 - February 29, 1960

Thomas Obediah Chisholm, author of *Living For Jesus* (page 169), was born on a farm in Simpson County, Kentucky and at the age of sixteen taught in the little one room schoolhouse he had attended. When twenty-one young Chisholm took a job as associate editor of the weekly newspaper in Franklin, Kentucky. After attending evangelist H.C. Morrison's revival meeting in Franklin, he went to work for Morrison as editor of his *Pentecostal Herald*, in Louisville, Kentucky.

In 1903 Chisholm was ordained into the Methodist ministry. He became ill in 1904 and for the next five years lived with his family on a farm near Winona Lake, Indiana, where in 1909 he began selling life insurance.

In 1916 Chisholm moved to Vineland, New Jersey where he continued to sell insurance and do occasional preaching. In 1953 he retired and moved to the Methodist Home for the Aged in Ocean Grove, New Jersey.

During his career Thomas Obediah Chisholm wrote over twelve hundred hymns, eight hundred of which were published in religious periodicals. In addition to his famous hymn, *Living For Jesus*, Thomas Chisholm will also be remembered for his hymn, *Great Is Thy Faithfulness*.

Fairest Lord Jesus

From the German, 17th century

From Schlesische Volkslieder, 1842
Arr. by Richard S. Willis, 1819-1900

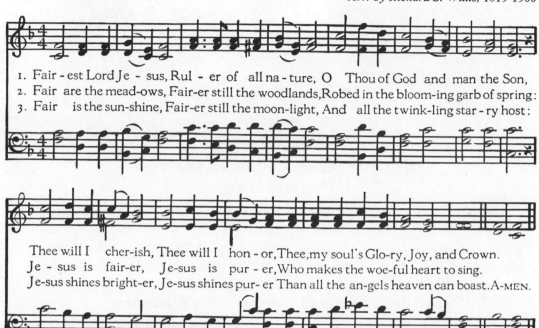

1. Fair - est Lord Je - sus, Rul - er of all na - ture, O Thou of God and man the Son,
2. Fair are the mead-ows, Fair-er still the woodlands, Robed in the bloom-ing garb of spring:
3. Fair is the sun-shine, Fair-er still the moon-light, And all the twink-ling star-ry host:

Thee will I cher-ish, Thee will I hon - or, Thee, my soul's Glo-ry, Joy, and Crown.
Je - sus is fair-er, Je-sus is pur - er, Who makes the woe-ful heart to sing.
Je-sus shines bright-er, Je-sus shines pur- er Than all the an-gels heaven can boast. A-MEN.

Augustus Lutheran Church, Trappe, Pennsylvania

The oldest Lutheran church building in the United States was erected in 1743 when after eleven years of meeting in a barn, the Lutherans in Trappe joined with those in New Hanover and Philadelphia to request the Inner Mission Institutions of Halle, Germany, to send a pastor. After his arrival in November of 1742, the men, women and children built Augustus Lutheran Church (seating four hundred and fifty persons) and held their first service September 12, 1743.

171

The Little Brown Church In The Vale
Nashua, Iowa

The Little Brown Church In The Vale is one of the few hymns extolling the virtues of being a part of a church community as a child and as an adult. "No place is so dear to my childhood ... Its tones so sweetly are calling ... Wing my way to the mansion of light ...". These words of William Pitts have, since they were first sung, struck a responsive, nostalgic chord in all Christians who heard them.

The hymn was born in June of 1857, when the stagecoach to Fredericksburg, Iowa, stopped at the thriving town of Bradford, Iowa. Here, while waiting for the journey to visit his fiancee to resume, William Pitts was touched by the serenity and beauty of the countryside and pictured a little brown church there in the vale. The thought lingered for months until finally he wrote this beautiful hymn.

Then, six years later, returning to teach music at the Bradford Academy, Pitts saw The First Congregational Church being built on the very spot mentioned in his hymn. At the church's dedication service in 1864 *The Little Brown Church In The Vale* was sung and from that time to this, the church and hymn have been one.

As years went by, William Pitts left Bradford and became a doctor in Fredericksburg. Even the town of Bradford died when the railroad went instead to nearby Nashua. But, The Little Brown Church in the Vale stands today, exactly as it did over one hundred years ago, surrounded by towering pines. The nearest town is two miles away.

The church's rustic wooden benches seat about one hundred and fifty people. Just enough for its congregation, and the visitors from far and wide who stay for Sunday services, while thousands of others visit during the week. And, the church bell "Its tones so sweetly are calling", rings especially sweet for the seven hundred or more couples married there each year, for after the wedding, the couple pulls together the time-worn rope, ringing the bell of The Little Brown Church In The Vale.

The Little Brown Church In The Vale

William S. Pitts   *William S. Pitts*

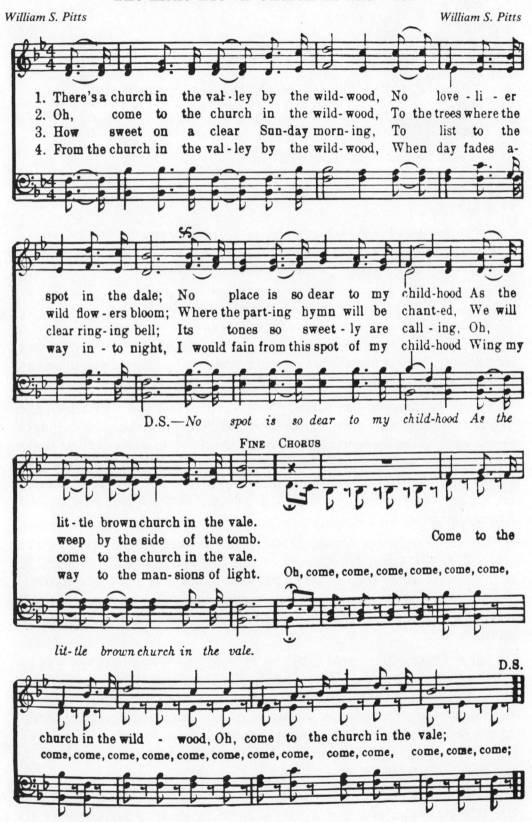

1. There's a church in the val-ley by the wild-wood, No love - li - er
2. Oh, come to the church in the wild-wood, To the trees where the
3. How sweet on a clear Sun-day morn-ing, To list to the
4. From the church in the val-ley by the wild-wood, When day fades a-

spot in the dale; No place is so dear to my child-hood As the
wild flow-ers bloom; Where the part-ing hymn will be chant-ed, We will
clear ring-ing bell; Its tones so sweet-ly are call-ing, Oh,
way in-to night, I would fain from this spot of my child-hood Wing my

D.S.—*No spot is so dear to my child-hood As the*

FINE CHORUS

lit-tle brown church in the vale.
weep by the side of the tomb.
come to the church in the vale.
way to the man-sions of light.   Come to the

Oh, come, come, come, come, come, come,

lit-tle brown church in the vale.

D.S.

church in the wild - wood, Oh, come to the church in the vale;
come, come, come, come, come, come, come, come, come, come, come, come, come;

173

FANNY JANE CROSBY

March 24, 1820 - February 12, 1915

When asked how she came to write *Blessed Assurance*, Fanny Crosby replied:

"In the year 1873 I wrote 'Blessed Assurance'. My friend, Mrs. Joseph F. Knapp, composed a melody and played it over to me two or three times on the piano. She then asked what it said, I replied: Blessed assurance, Jesus is mine!
O What a foretaste of glory divine!
Heir of salvation, purchase of God,
Born of His spirit, washed in His blood.''

Such was the gift of Fanny Crosby who although blind since infancy was America's best known hymn writer, composing some eight thousand hymns during her life.

Fanny was born in South East, New York. When she was fifteen she entered the New York City School for the Blind where she soon began to develop her talent for writing lyric poems. At first she wrote secular songs and earned three thousand dollars in royalties for her popular, *Rosalie, The Prairie Flower.* After graduation, Fanny stayed at the School for the Blind for eleven years teaching English grammar, rhetoric and Roman and American history.

In 1858 Fanny married Alexander Van Alstyne, a musician who was also blind. Six years later she met the famous composer William B. Bradbury and at his request wrote her first hymn at the age of forty-one. The hymn was a success and Fanny, feeling that she had found her real mission in life, wrote to a friend saying she was "the happiest creature in all the land".

Fanny Crosby spent most of her life in New York City where she was an active member of the John Street Methodist Episcopal Church (America's oldest Methodist church pictured on page 176). As years went by her name became a magic formula for success to music composers and publishers. At one point, she was under contract to produce three hymns per week and while so doing, she still provided hymns for her composer friends, Bradbury, Root, Doane, Lowry, Sankey and others.

Fanny Crosby lived a radiant life, all ninety-five years of it, and spent her last few years at her daughter's home in Bridgeport, Connecticut, writing her beloved hymns.

Blessed Assurance

Fanny J. Crosby, 1820-1915

Mrs. Joseph F. Knapp, 1839-1908

1. Bless-ed as-sur-ance, Je-sus is mine! O what a fore-taste of glo-ry di-vine! Heir of sal-va-tion, pur-chase of God, Born of His Spir-it, washed in His blood.

2. Per-fect sub-mis-sion, per-fect de-light, Vi-sions of rap-ture now burst on my sight; An-gels de-scend-ing, bring from a-bove, Ech-oes of mer-cy, whis-pers of love.

3. Per-fect sub-mis-sion, all is at rest, I in my Sav-iour am hap-py and blest, Watch-ing and wait-ing, look-ing a-bove, Filled with His good-ness, lost in His love.

REFRAIN

This is my sto-ry, this is my song, Prais-ing my Sav-iour all the day long; This is my sto-ry, this is my song, Praising my Sav-iour all the day long. Amen.

Doane **Bradbury** **Lowry**

The music to the three following hymns was written by two of Fanny Crosby's favorite composers, William Doane (page 142) and Robert Lowry (page 138). Her friend Bradbury's biography is on page 136.

John Street United Methodist Church
The Oldest Methodist Society In America

Before coming to America in 1760, Philip Embury of Ballangrane, Ireland, received his preacher's license from John Wesley. The Embury's settled in New York City and by 1766, Philip began holding church services. In March of 1768, the Society bought the John Street property and on the last Sunday in October, the first services were held at the John Street Church.

Draw Me Nearer

Fanny J. Crosby　　　　　　　　　　　　　　　　　　　*William H. Doane*

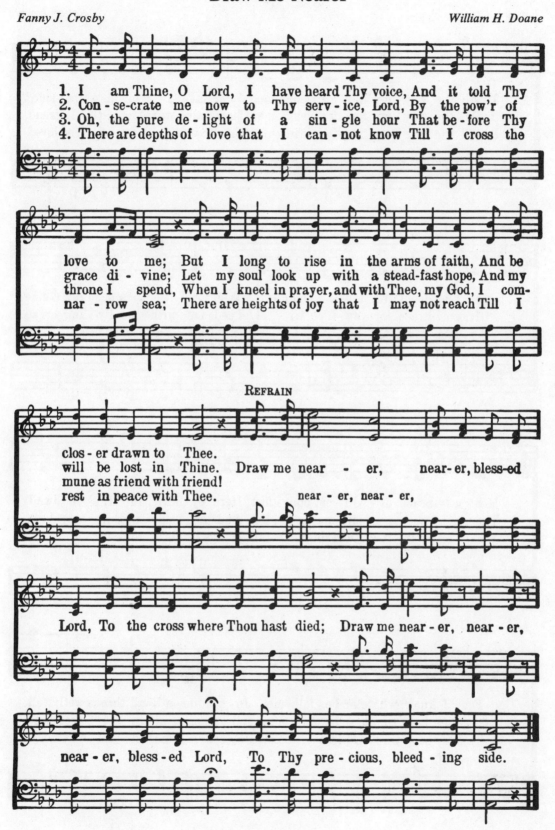

1. I am Thine, O Lord, I have heard Thy voice, And it told Thy
2. Con - se-crate me now to Thy serv - ice, Lord, By the pow'r of
3. Oh, the pure de - light of a sin - gle hour That be - fore Thy
4. There are depths of love that I can - not know Till I cross the

love to me; But I long to rise in the arms of faith, And be
grace di - vine; Let my soul look up with a stead-fast hope, And my
throne I spend, When I kneel in prayer, and with Thee, my God, I com-
nar - row sea; There are heights of joy that I may not reach Till I

REFRAIN

clos - er drawn to Thee.
will be lost in Thine. Draw me near - er, near - er, bless-ed
mune as friend with friend!
rest in peace with Thee. near - er, near - er,

Lord, To the cross where Thou hast died; Draw me near - er, near - er,

near - er, bless - ed Lord, To Thy pre - cious, bleed - ing side.

All the Way My Savior Leads Me

Fanny J. Crosby   *Robert Lowry*

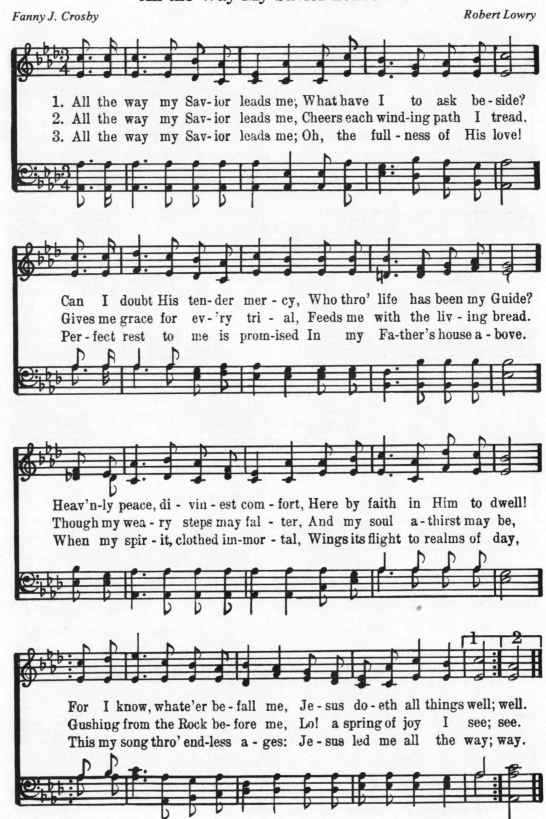

1. All the way my Sav-ior leads me; What have I to ask be-side?
2. All the way my Sav-ior leads me, Cheers each wind-ing path I tread.
3. All the way my Sav-ior leads me; Oh, the full-ness of His love!

Can I doubt His ten-der mer-cy, Who thro' life has been my Guide?
Gives me grace for ev-'ry tri-al, Feeds me with the liv-ing bread.
Per-fect rest to me is prom-ised In my Fa-ther's house a-bove.

Heav'n-ly peace, di-vin-est com-fort, Here by faith in Him to dwell!
Though my wea-ry steps may fal-ter, And my soul a-thirst may be,
When my spir-it, clothed im-mor-tal, Wings its flight to realms of day,

For I know, whate'er be-fall me, Je-sus do-eth all things well; well.
Gushing from the Rock be-fore me, Lo! a spring of joy I see; see.
This my song thro' end-less a-ges: Je-sus led me all the way; way.

To God Be the Glory

CAROLINA V. SANDELL BERG

October 3, 1832 - July 27, 1903

Lina Sandell, the Fanny Crosby of Sweden, was born at Fröderyd, Sweden where her father was the parish minister. When she was twenty-six Lina took a trip with her father to Gothenburg. While en route, he fell overboard and drowned right before her eyes. The tragedy had a profound effect on Lina's life. In the midst of her grief, hymns poured forth from the depths of her broken heart. Fourteen of these hymns were published and although Lina wrote six hundred and fifty hymns during her life, these fourteen, including the beautiful *Children Of The Heavenly Father*, have always been the most popular.

In 1867 Lina Sandell married C. O. Berg, a Stockholm merchant, but continued to sign her hymns with the initials, "L.S.".

Lina Sandells' hymns became popular in America and elsewhere when Jenny Lind, the "Swedish Nightingale" who, like Lina was a Pietist, not only sang Lina's hymns but financed the first edition of *Ahnfelt's Songs*, which consisted mostly of Lina Sandell's hymns.

OSKAR AHNFELT

Sweden's

"Spiritual Troubadour"

playing his famous
12 string guitar

Oskar Ahnfelt composed or arranged the music for all Lina Sandell's hymns and traveled throughout the Scandinavian countries singing them. Due to strong opposition from State Church officials to these Pietistic hymns, Ahnfelt was ordered to sing Lina's hymns to the King. When Ahnfelt finished singing, King Karl XV said, "You may sing as much as you desire in both of my kingdoms." And sing he did, as Lina Sandell said, "Ahnfelt has sung my songs into the hearts of the people."

Children Of The Heavenly Father

Caroline V. Sandell Berg   *Arr: Oscar Ahnfelt*

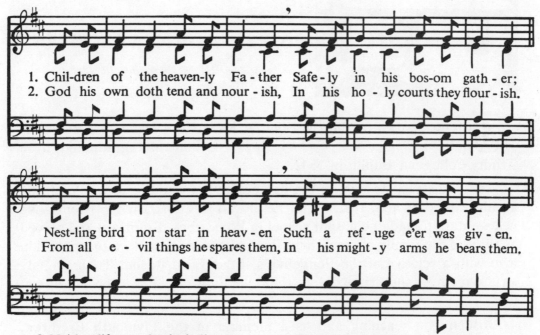

1. Chil-dren of the heaven-ly Fa-ther Safe-ly in his bos-om gath-er;
2. God his own doth tend and nour-ish, In his ho-ly courts they flour-ish.

Nest-ling bird nor star in heav-en Such a ref-uge e'er was giv-en.
From all e-vil things he spares them, In his might-y arms he bears them.

3 Neither life nor death shall ever
From the Lord his children sever;
Unto them his grace he showeth,
And their sorrows all he knoweth.

4 Though he giveth or he taketh,
God his children ne'er forsaketh,
His the loving purpose solely
To preserve them pure and holy.

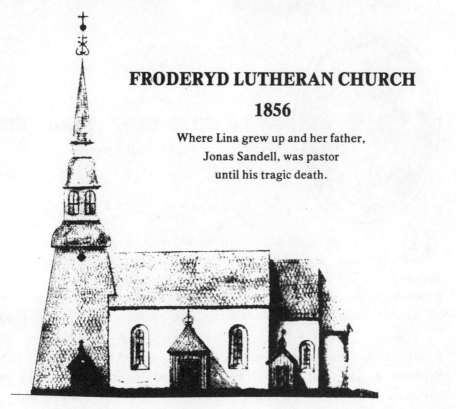

FRODERYD LUTHERAN CHURCH

1856

Where Lina grew up and her father,
Jonas Sandell, was pastor
until his tragic death.

181

JOSEPH MEDLICOTT SCRIVEN

September 10, 1819 - August 10, 1886

Joseph Scriven, author of *What A Friend We Have In Jesus,* was born in Seapatrick, County Down, Ireland and graduated from Trinity College at Dublin in 1842.

Tragedy struck Joseph on the day before his wedding when his bride accidentally drowned. Distraught, he moved to Canada when twenty-five years old. In Canada he taught school in Woodstock, Brantford and served as tutor to the family of Lieutenant Pengelley near Bewdley. Joseph fell in love with a relative of the Pengelley's, Miss Eliza Roche. Then tragedy struck again. A short time before their wedding day, Eliza became ill and died.

Joseph quit teaching and as a member of the Plymouth Brethren, devoted most of his time to doing menial work for the aged, accepting no payment in return. He lived out his years alone in this little white cottage in Port Hope, Canada, where, in 1855, he wrote *What A Friend We Have In Jesus* for his mother in Ireland.

CHARLES CROZAT CONVERSE

October 7, 1832 - October 18, 1918

Charles Converse was born at Warren, Massachusetts. He went to Europe to attend the Leipzig Conservatory and upon his return to America studied law, graduating from Albany University in 1861. He spent most of his life in Erie, Pennsylvania where he engaged in a wide variety of interests which included philosophy and philology as well as music.

During his career he composed string quartets, patriotic overtures, vocal compositions, chorales and hymn tunes often for Ira D. Sankey's or William B. Bradbury's Sunday school publications. Converse composed the music for *What A Friend We Have In Jesus,* for *Silver Wings* (1870) but it did not become famous until published in Gospel Hymns (1875).

What A Friend We Have In Jesus

Joseph Scriven   *Charles C. Converse*

1. What a Friend we have in Je-sus, All our sins and griefs to bear!
2. Have we tri-als and temp-ta-tions? Is there trou-ble an-y-where?
3. Are we weak and heav-y la-den, Cum-bered with a load of care?

What a priv-i-lege to car-ry Ev-ery-thing to God in prayer!
We should nev-er be dis-cour-aged: Take it to the Lord in prayer.
Pre-cious Sav-iour, still our Ref-uge— Take it to the Lord in prayer.

O what peace we oft-en for-feit, O what need-less pain we bear,
Can we find a friend so faith-ful Who will all our sor-rows share?
Do thy friends de-spise, for-sake thee? Take it to the Lord in prayer!

All be-cause we do not car-ry Ev-ery-thing to God in prayer!
Je-sus knows our ev-ery weak-ness: Take it to the Lord in prayer. A-men.
In His arms He'll take and shield thee, Thou wilt find a sol-ace there.

HENRY ERNEST NICHOL

December 10, 1862 - 1928

ublished in London in *The Sunday School Hymnary* in 1896, Ernest Nichols inspiring hymn, *We've A Story To Tell To The Nations* soon became a favorite of Christians everywhere.

Henry Ernest Nichol was born in Hull, England. Loving music he decided to give up his intended career as a civil engineer and received his Bachelor of Music degree from Oxford University in 1888.

During his career he wrote a great number of tunes, most of them for Sunday school services. Whenever he wrote both the words and the music for a hymn he would sign his name "Colin Sterne" on the left (author's side) and Ernest Nichol on the right (composer's side). Of all his works only one hymn remains, but that one hymn is the ever popular *We've A Story To Tell To The Nations*.

We've A Story To Tell To The Nations

"Colin Sterne"

H. Ernest Nichol
Adapted

1. We've a sto - ry to tell to the na - tions That shall
2. We've a song to be sung to the na - tions, That shall
3. We've a mes - sage to give to the na - tions, That the
4. We've a Sav - iour to show to the na - tions, Who the

We've A Story To Tell To The Nations [continued]

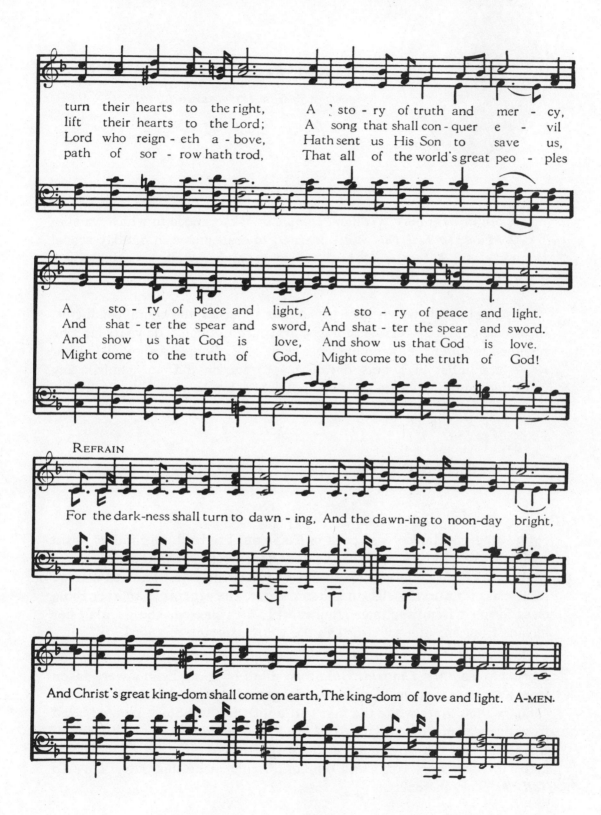

turn their hearts to the right, A story of truth and mercy,
lift their hearts to the Lord; A song that shall conquer evil
Lord who reigneth above, Hath sent us His Son to save us,
path of sorrow hath trod, That all of the world's great peoples

A story of peace and light, A story of peace and light.
And shatter the spear and sword, And shatter the spear and sword.
And show us that God is love, And show us that God is love.
Might come to the truth of God, Might come to the truth of God!

REFRAIN

For the darkness shall turn to dawning, And the dawning to noonday bright,

And Christ's great kingdom shall come on earth, The kingdom of love and light. A-MEN.

WILLIAM GUSTAVUS FISCHER

October 14, 1835 - August 12, 1912

Born in Baltimore, William, composer of the music to which we sing *I Love To Tell The Story,* learned to read music in Sunday school singing class. Later he studied music at night, while working for a bookbinder during the day.

Fischer became widely known as a music teacher and choral conductor. In 1858 he became professor of music at Girard College. Ten years later he resigned to enter the piano business with J. E. Gould. Although Fischer wrote a number of hymns during his career he did not publish any collections other than the leaflets published for Sunday schools by his company, Fischer and Gould.

ARABELLA CATHERINE [KATHERINE] HANKEY

1834 - May 9, 1911

Katherine Hankey was born in Clapham, England. Her father was a banker and member of the Clapham Sect of Evangelicals. As a young girl, Kate taught Sunday school and at eighteen organized a large Bible class for working girls in London. Later, she organized another Bible class for girls from wealthier families. As years passed, she gave all her income from her literary efforts to the church foreign missions.

Katherine Hankey will always be remembered for *I Love To Tell The Story* and *Tell Me The Old, Old Story.* Both of these hymns were taken from Katherine's poem *The Old, Old Story* dealing with the life of Jesus. In January 1866 Kate wrote the first part entitled, "The Story Wanted" and from this was made the hymn *Tell Me The Old, Old Story* by William H. Doane in 1867. In November Kate wrote the second part of the poem entitled, "The Story Told" and William Fischer made this into *I Love To Tell The Story* in 1869.

I Love To Tell The Story

Katherine Hankey   *William G. Fischer*

1. I love to tell the sto - ry Of un - seen things a - bove, Of
2. I love to tell the sto - ry; More won - der - ful it seems Than
3. I love to tell the sto - ry; 'Tis pleas - ant to re - peat What
4. I love to tell the sto - ry, For those who know it best Seem

Je - sus and His glo - ry, Of Je - sus and His love. I love to tell the
all the gold-en fan - cies Of all our gold-en dreams. I love to tell the
seems, each time I tell it, More won-der-ful-ly sweet. I love to tell the
hun - ger - ing and thirst-ing To hear it like the rest. And when, in scenes of

sto - ry, Be - cause I know 'tis true; It sat - is - fies my long-ings
sto - ry, It did so much for me; And that is just the rea - son
sto - ry, For some have nev - er heard The mes - sage of sal - va - tion
glo - ry, I sing the new, new song, 'Twill be the old, old sto - ry

REFRAIN

As noth - ing else can do. I love to tell the sto - ry, 'Twill be my theme in glo-ry,
I tell it now to thee.
From God's own ho-ly Word.
That I have loved so long.

To tell the old, old sto - ry Of Je - sus and His love. A - MEN.

C. AUSTIN MILES

January 7, 1868 - March 10, 1946

C. Austin Miles, author of *In The Garden*, was author of several of the most popular gospel hymns of his day. He was born in Lakehurst, New Jersey in 1868. At the age of sixteen he wanted to train for the ministry but circumstances forced him to take a job with a pharmacy.

In 1892 he wrote his first gospel hymn, *List 'Tis Jesus' Voice* and when a man was converted due to hearing this hymn at a revival meeting, Austin Miles was convinced that God had been speaking to him in various ways for a long time.

In March of 1898 he took *List 'Tis Jesus' Voice* and other hymns he had composed to Hall-Mack Company, religious music publishers. They purchased his works and in June of that year hired C. Austin Miles to work full-time writing, editing, composing and promoting gospel hymns.

Although Miles wrote various cantatas and anthems during his career, he said, "It is as a writer of gospel songs I am proud to be known, for in that way I may be of the most use to my Master, whom I serve willingly although not as efficiently as is my desire".

C. Austin Miles usually wrote both the words and music for his hymns as did many of the other famous evangelistic musicians of his day. When he wrote *In The Garden* in 1912, it was an immediate success and as the years pass by it continues to be a famous hymn.

In The Garden

C.A.M.   C. Austin Miles

1. I come to the gar-den a-lone, While the dew is still on the
2. He speaks, and the sound of His voice Is so sweet the birds hush their
3. I'd stay in the gar-den with Him Tho' the night a-round me be

ros - es, And the voice I hear, Fall-ing on my ear, The
sing - ing, And the mel - o - dy That He gave to me, With-
fall - ing, But He bids me go; Thro' the voice of woe His

Son of God dis - clos - es.
in my heart is ring - ing.   **CHORUS** And He walks with me, and He
voice to me is call - ing.

talks with me, And He tells me I am His own; And the

joy we share as we tar - ry there, None oth - er has ev - er known.

JOSEPH HENRY GILMORE

April 29, 1834 - July 23, 1918

In the words of the author Joseph Gilmore here's how the inspiring hymn, *He Leadeth Me!*, was written:

"As a young man who recently had been graduated from Brown University and Newton Theological Institution, I was supplying for a couple of Sundays the pulpit of the First Baptist Church in Philadelphia. At the midweek service -- on the 26th of March, 1862 -- I set out to give the people an exposition of the 23rd Psalm. . . . but this time I did not get further than the words 'He Leadeth Me'. Those words took hold of me as they had never done before. I saw in them a significance and beauty of which I had never dreamed . . . At the close of the meeting . . . I penciled the hymn, handed it to my wife and thought no more about it . . . It occurred to her months afterward to send the hymn to the *Watchman and Reflector* . . . In that paper it attracted the attention of William B. Bradbury, who slightly modified the refrain and set the hymn to the music."

Joseph Gilmore was born in Massachusetts and educated at Phillips Academy, Brown University and Newton Theological Seminary. After graduating from Newton he remained for one year to teach Hebrew. Ordained in the Baptist ministry in 1862, he became pastor of the Baptist church in Fisherville, New Hampshire.

In 1863-1864, during his father's term as Governor of New Hampshire, Joseph served as his assistant and as editor of the Concord *Daily Monitor*.

In 1865 he became pastor of the Second Baptist Church in Rochester, New York and two years later he was invited to also serve as acting professor of Hebrew at the Rochester Theological Seminary. The following year he was appointed professor of logic, rhetoric and English literature at the University of Rochester and he remained in this position until his retirement in 1908.

Joseph Henry Gilmore was the author of six books and several hymns but will always be remembered for *He Leadeth Me!*, the hymn he wrote when he was only twenty-eight years old and a visiting preacher in Philadelphia.

The biography of William Batchelder Bradbury, who composed the music to which we sing *He Leadeth Me!*, appears on page 136.

He Leadeth Me

Joseph H. Gilmore   *William B. Bradbury*

1. He lead-eth me! O bless-ed tho't! O words with heav'nly comfort fraught!
2. Sometimes 'mid scenes of deepest gloom, Some-times where E-den's bowers bloom.
3. Lord, I would clasp Thy hand in mine, Nor ev - er mur - mur nor re - pine,
4. And when my task on earth is done, When, by Thy grace, the vic-t'ry's won,

What-e'er I do, wher-e'er I be,   Still 'tis God's hand that lead-eth me.
By wa - ters still, o'er troub-led sea,— Still 'tis His hand that lead-eth me!
Con - tent, what-ev - er lot I see,   Since 'tis my God that lead-eth me!
E'en death's cold wave I will not flee,   Since God thro' Jor-dan lead-eth me.

REFRAIN

He lead-eth me, He lead-eth me, By His own hand He lead-eth me:

His faith-ful fol-lower I would be, For by His hand He lead-eth me.

GEORGE BENNARD

February 4, 1873 - October 10, 1958

George Bennard, author and composer of *The Old Rugged Cross,* was born in Youngstown, Ohio, the son of a coal miner. As a small child his family moved to Albia, Iowa and later Lucas, Iowa. While attending a Salvation Army meeting in Lucas, young George decided he wanted to become an evangelist but when sixteen years old his father died, leaving him as sole support for his mother and four sisters. They moved to Illinois, where later George married and he and his wife, Hannah, became Salvation Army workers. After several years he resigned and joined the Methodist Episcopal Church and worked for many years as an evangelist in the United States and Canada before retiring to Reed City, Michigan.

During his career he wrote over three hundred hymns to which either he or his wife Hannah wrote the music. George Bennard will always be remembered for the hymn he wrote in 1913, *The Old Rugged Cross.* Here is his story of that event:

> "I was praying for a full understanding of the cross, and its plan in Christianity. I read and studied and prayed. I saw Christ and the Cross inseparably ... It was like seeing John 3:16 leave the printed page, take form, and act out the meaning of redemption. While watching this scene with my mind's eye, the theme of the song came to me, and with it the melody; but only the words of the theme, 'The Old Rugged Cross' ... I was holding evangelistic meetings in Michigan, but could not continue with the poem. After a series of meetings in New York state, the following week, I tried again to compose the poem, but could not. It was only after I ... returned to Michigan for further evangelistic work, that the flood-gates were loosed ..."

In honor of George Bennard, the Reed City, Michigan, Chamber of Commerce erected a twenty foot cross on US 131 bearing the words: "The Old Rugged Cross" and "Home of Living Author, Rev. Geo. Bennard." The cross was publicly dedicated and later wired for lighting.

The Old Rugged Cross

George Bennard   *George Bennard*

1. On a hill far a-way stood an old rug-ged cross, The em-blem of
2. Oh, that old rug-ged cross, so de-spised by the world, Has a won-drous at-
3. In the old rug-ged cross, stained with blood so di-vine, A won-drous
4. To the old rug-ged cross I will ev-er be true, Its shame and re-

suf-fering and shame; And I love that old cross where the dear-est and best
trac-tion for me; For the dear Lamb of God left His glo-ry a-bove
beau-ty I see; For 'twas on that old cross Je-sus suf-fered and died
proach glad-ly bear; Then He'll call me some day to my home far a-way,

CHORUS

For a world of lost sin-ners was slain.
To bear it to dark Cal-va-ry.   So I'll cher-ish the old rug-ged
To par-don and sanc-ti-fy me.
Where His glo-ry for-ev-er I'll share.   cross, the

cross,........ Till my tro-phies at last I lay down; I will cling to the
old rug-ged cross,

old rug-ged cross,.......... And ex-change it some day for a crown.
cross, the old rug-ged cross,

KNOWLES SHAW

October 13, 1834 - June 7, 1878

orn in Butler County, Ohio, Knowles family moved shortly after his birth to Rush County, Indiana where his father, Albin, was a farmer and tanner.

When he was only twelve years old Knowles father became very ill, he called Knowles, gave him his most prized possession, his violin and admonished him, "be good to your mother". Within a few days he passed away. Knowles, being the oldest, went to work on the farm to help support his mother and two sisters. Knowles learned to play his father's violin and whenever he could played at parties and dances until soon he was making more money as a fiddler than as a farmer.

On September 13, 1852, Knowles life changed direction when he was baptized at the Flat Rock Church. Knowles began preaching in 1858 and became widely known as the "Singing Evangelist". In 1874 he became pastor of a Christian (Disciples of Christ) church in Chicago but resigned to return to evangelism.

In June of 1878 Knowles had just completed a successful five week revival meeting in Dallas, Texas, at the Commerce Street Christian Church (Disciples of Christ) and was on his way to join his family in Columbus, Mississippi, when just this side of McKinney, Texas, a broken rail caused the derailment of the car in which he was riding, injuring twenty-seven passengers and killing Knowles Shaw.

Of the five collections of Sunday school hymns he published *Bringing In The Sheaves,* from his *The Morning Star* collection of 1877, lives on as one of our most loved hymns.

The biography of the composer, George A. Minor is on page 196.

Bringing In The Sheaves

Knowles Shaw

George A. Minor

1. Sow - ing in the morn - ing, sow-ing seeds of kind-ness, Sow-ing in the
2. Sow - ing in the sun - shine, sow-ing in the shad - ows, Fear-ing nei - ther
3. Go - ing forth with weep-ing, sow-ing for the Mas - ter, Tho' the loss sus-

noon - tide and the dew - y eve; Wait-ing for the har - vest,
clouds nor win-ter's chill - ing breeze; By and by the har - vest,
tained our spir - it oft - en grieves; When our weep-ing's o - ver,

and the time of reap-ing, We shall come re - joic-ing, bring-ing in the sheaves.
and the la - bor end - ed, We shall come re - joic-ing, bring-ing in the sheaves.
He will bid us wel-come, We shall come re - joic-ing, bring-ing in the sheaves.

CHORUS

Bring-ing in the sheaves, bring-ing in the sheaves, We shall come re-joic-
Bring-ing in the sheaves, bring-ing in the sheaves, We shall come re-joic-

1 ing, bring - ing in the sheaves; *2* ing, bring-ing in the sheaves.

GEORGE A. MINOR

December 7, 1845 - January 29, 1904

Born in Richmond, Virginia, George Minor, composer of the music for *Bringing In The Sheaves,* was educated at a military academy in Richmond and served in Virginia's Army of the Potomac during the Civil War. After the war he taught vocal music, conducted singing schools and music conventions. Later he became one of the founders of Hume-Minor Company, piano and organ manufacturers.

George Minor was a member of the First Baptist Church of Richmond where he served as chairman of the music committee and music leader for the Sunday school. Among his several published collections are *Golden Light, No. 1* (1879), *Golden Light No. 2, Golden Light No. 3* (1884), *Standard Songs* (1896) and a collection of songs for small children, *The Rosebud.*

EDWARD HOPPER

February 17, 1816 - April 23, 1888

Published anonymously in *The Sailor's Magazine* of March 3, 1871, *Jesus, Saviour Pilot Me* has long been known as "The Sailor's Hymn".

Its author, later identified as Edward Hopper, was born in New York City in 1816 and educated at New York University. Following graduation from Union Theological Seminary in 1842 he became a Presbyterian minister. Hopper served at Greenville, New York, Sag Harbor, and Long Island before coming to the Church Of The Land and Sea in New York City, his last pastorate, where he wrote his beautiful *Jesus, Saviour Pilot Me.*

JOHN EDGAR GOULD

1822 - March 4, 1875

Born in Bangor, Maine, John Gould became a composer, publisher and merchant in New York City. In 1868 he moved to Philadelphia and opened a piano and music business with William G. Fischer (composer of the tune for *I Love To Tell The Story,* page 186).

With Edward L. White he compiled *The Modern Harp* (1846), *The Wreath Of School Songs* (1847), *The Tyrolian Lyre* (1847), *The Sunday School Lute* (1848), *Harmonia Sacra* (1851) and *Songs Of Gladness for the Sabbath School* (1869).

Jesus, Savior, Pilot Me

Edward Hopper   *John E. Gould*

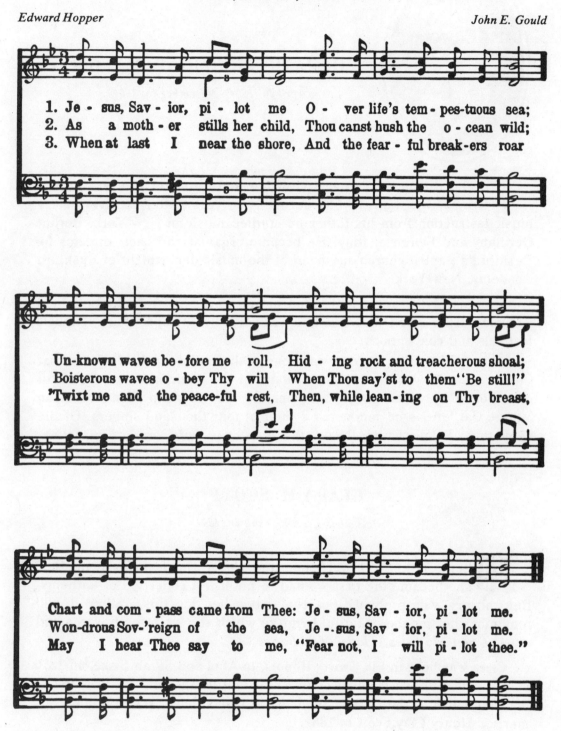

1. Je - sus, Sav - ior, pi - lot me O - ver life's tem - pes-tuous sea;
2. As a moth - er stills her child, Thou canst hush the o - cean wild;
3. When at last I near the shore, And the fear - ful break-ers roar

Un-known waves be - fore me roll, Hid - ing rock and treacherous shoal;
Boisterous waves o - bey Thy will When Thou say'st to them "Be still!"
'Twixt me and the peace-ful rest, Then, while lean-ing on Thy breast,

Chart and com - pass came from Thee: Je - sus, Sav - ior, pi - lot me.
Won-drous Sov-'reign of the sea, Je - sus, Sav - ior, pi - lot me.
May I hear Thee say to me, "Fear not, I will pi - lot thee."

HORATIO RICHMOND PALMER

April 26, 1834 - November 15, 1907

oratio Richmond Palmer, publisher and promoter of Clara Scott's hymns, was born in Sherburne, New York. After receiving early music instruction from his father he studied music in New York, Berlin, Germany and Florence, Italy. He became organist and choir director for Rushford's Baptist church and head of the music department of Rushford Academy, New York.

After the Civil War he moved to Chicago where he wrote books, edited a music journal, *The Concordia,* and was very successful conducting music festivals and conventions.

From 1877 to 1891 Palmer was dean of the summer school of music at Chautauqua, New York. He also organized the Church Choral Union of New York City which gave huge concerts, one of them filling Madison Square Garden as he conducted a choir of four thousand singers. Of the hymn tunes Palmer wrote the one that lives on is *Yield Not To Temptation.*

CLARA H. SCOTT

December 3, 1841 - June 21, 1897

hen Clara Scott published the *Royal Anthem Book* in 1882 she became the first woman to publish a collection of anthems. But, history will probably not remember her for this, rather it will remember her for the beautiful hymn to which she wrote both words and music *Open My Eyes, That I May See.*

Clara was born in Elk Grove, Illinois, to Abel and Sarah Fiske. In 1856 she attended the first musical institute in Chicago and in 1859 began teaching music at the Ladies' Seminary at Lyons, Iowa. While in Iowa she married Henry Clay Scott in 1861.

She became acquainted with the great musician Horatio R. Palmer who encouraged her writing and included a large number of her songs into his collections for publication. During her career Clara published three collections before she was thrown from a buggy by a runaway horse and tragically killed, near Dubuque, Iowa.

Open My Eyes, That I May See

Clara H. Scott   *Clara H. Scott*

1. O - pen my eyes, that I   may see Glimps-es of truth Thou hast for me;
2. O - pen my ears, that I   may hear Voic - es of truth Thou send-est clear;
3. O - pen my mouth, and let   me bear Glad - ly the warm truth ev-ery-where;

Place in my hands the won-der - ful key That shall un-clasp, and set me free.
And while the wave-notes fall on my ear, Ev - ery-thing false will dis - ap-pear.
O - pen my heart, and let me pre-pare Love with Thy chil-dren thus to share.

Si - lent-ly now I wait for Thee, Read-y, my God, Thy will   to see;

O - pen my eyes, il - lu - mine me, Spir - it di - vine!
O - pen my ears, il - lu - mine me, Spir - it di - vine!
O - pen my heart, il - lu - mine me, Spir - it di - vine!   A - MEN.

JAMES MILTON BLACK

August 19, 1856 - December 21, 1938

Born in South Hill, New York, James Black was a teacher of singing schools and edited twelve gospel hymn books. Black was a very active Methodist layman and here, in his words is the story of *When The Roll Is Called Up Yonder:*

"While a teacher in a Sunday-school and president of a young people's society, I one day met a girl, fourteen years, poorly clad and the child of a drunkard. She accepted my invitation to attend Sunday-school ... One evening at a consecration meeting, when members answered the roll call by repeating Scripture texts, she failed to respond. I spoke of what a sad thing it would be, when our names are called from the Lamb's Book of Life, if one of us should be absent ... I longed for something suitable to sing just then, but I could find nothing in the books. We closed the meeting ... When I reached my house my wife saw that I was deeply troubled, and questioned me, but I made no reply. Then the words of the first stanza came to me in full. In fifteen minutes more I had composed the other two verses. Going to the piano, I played the music just as it is found today in the hymn-book, note for note, and I have never dared to change a single word or a note of the piece since."

When the Roll is Called up Yonder

J.M.B.   *James M. Black*

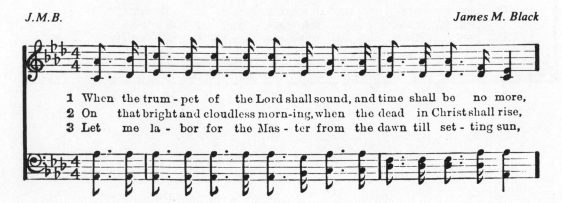

200

When the Roll is Called up Yonder [continued]

And the morn - ing breaks, e - ter - nal, bright and fair; When the
And the glo - ry of His res - ur - rec - tion share; When His
Let me talk of all His won - drous love and care, Then, when

saved of earth shall gath - er o - ver on the oth - er shore And the
chos - en ones shall gath - er to their home be - yond the skies, And the
all of life is o - ver, and my work on earth is done, And the

CHORUS.

roll is called up yon - der, I'll be there. }
roll is called up yon - der, I'll be there. } When the roll....... is called up
roll is called up yon - der, I'll be there. } When the roll is called up

yon - - der, When the roll....... is called up yon - - der, When the
yon - der, I'll be there,   When the roll is called up yon - der, I'll be there,

roll....... is called up yon - der, When the roll is called up yonder, I'll be there.
When the roll

RUSSELL KELSO CARTER

November 18, 1849 - August 23, 1926

Russell Carter, author and composer of *Standing On The Promises,* was born in Baltimore, Maryland, and graduated from the first class of Pennsylvania Military Academy in Chester, Pennsylvania. After graduation in 1867 he remained at Pennsylvania Military becoming an instructor in 1869 and professor of natural sciences and chemistry in 1872. In 1873 he took leave, went to California and raised sheep until 1876. He returned to Pennsylvania Military Academy and in 1881 became professor of higher mathematics and civil engineering.

Russell resigned from Pennsylvania Military Academy in 1887 and was ordained into the Methodist ministry where he joined with the Holiness movement, becoming very active in camp meeting activities. After a number of years in the ministry, Russell's interest shifted to medicine and he became a physician in Baltimore, Maryland.

A brilliant man in many different disciplines, Russell Carter's literary output was prolific, writing novels as well as books on religion, mathematics and science. In hymnody, Carter's collection *Hymns Of The Christian Life* (1891) which he edited with A. B. Simpson is most remarkable. In this collection Carter contributed words and music for fifty-two hymns, the music for forty-four hymns by other writers and adapted the music for twenty-five other hymns.

During his brilliant career Russell Kelso Carter did many, many things. He was a professor, a writer, a musician, a minister and a doctor but he will always be remembered for the most loved hymn *Standing On The Promises* which he wrote one day in 1885 and published in his *Songs Of Perfect Love* compiled by he and John R. Sweney.

Standing on the Promises

R. Kelso Carter

R. Kelso Carter

1. Stand-ing on the prom-is-es of Christ my King, Through e-ter-nal a - ges
2. Stand-ing on the prom-is-es that can - not fail, When the howl-ing storms of
3. Stand-ing on the prom-is-es of Christ the Lord, Bound to Him e - ter - nal-
4. Stand-ing on the prom-is-es I can - not fall, Lis-tening ev-ery mo-ment

let His prais - es ring; Glo - ry in the high-est, I will shout and sing,
doubt and fear as - sail, By the liv - ing word of God I shall pre - vail,
ly by love's strong cord, O - ver-com-ing dai - ly with the Spir - it's sword,
to the Spir - it's call, Rest-ing in my Sav-iour as my all in all,

CHORUS

Stand-ing on the prom-is-es of God. Stand - - ing, stand - - ing,
Standing on the promises, standing on the promises,

Stand-ing on the prom-is-es of God my Sav-iour; Stand - - ing,
Standing on the prom-is-es,

stand - - ing, I'm stand-ing on the prom-is - es of God.
stand-ing on the prom-is - es,

GEORGE JAMES WEBB

June 24, 1803 - October 7, 1887

George James Webb, composer of the music for *Stand Up For Jesus*, was born at Wiltshire, England. In 1830 he came to the United States and settled in Boston. He became organist for Boston's old South Church and remained there for forty years. Here he became associated with Lowell Mason in the Boston Academy of Music, the training of music teachers and also in the compiling and editing of music collections.

GEORGE DUFFIELD, JR.

September 12, 1818 - July 6, 1888

George Duffield, author of *Stand Up For Jesus*, was born in Carlisle, Pennsylvania. Both his father and grandfather were Presbyterian ministers and George followed in the family tradition, attending Union Theological Seminary upon graduation from Yale University (B.A. 1837). He graduated from Union in 1840 and was ordained a Presbyterian minister that same year. During his long career he served pastorates in Brooklyn, New York, Bloomfield, New Jersey, Philadelphia, Pennsylvania, Adrian, Michigan, Galesburg, Illinois, Saginaw, Michigan and finally Lansing, Michigan in 1869. In 1884 he retired to Bloomfield, New Jersey, the home of his son, the Reverend Samuel W. Duffield.

In the forty-four year ministry of George Duffield the one sermon he preached in 1859, inspired by the tragic death of his good friend Reverend Dudley A. Tyng, stands as a monument to this career. Regarding this **(Continued under hymn on page 205.)**

Stand Up For Jesus

G. Duffield

G. J. Webb

1. Stand up, stand up for Je - sus, Ye sol-diers of the cross, Lift high His
2. Stand up, stand up for Je - sus, The trump-et call o - bey; Forth to the
3. Stand up, stand up for Je - sus—Stand in His strength a-lone; The arm of

roy - al ban - ner, It must not suf fer loss; From vic-t'ry un - to vic-t'ry, His
might-y con - flict, In this His glorious day."Ye that are men now serve Him," A-
flesh will fail you—Ye dare not trust your own; Put on the gos - pel ar - mor, And

ar - my shall He lead, Till ev-'ry foe is vanquished And Christ is Lord in-deed.
gainst unnumbered foes; Let courage rise with danger, And strength to strength oppose.
watching un - to prayer, Where du-ty calls, or dan-ger, Be nev-er want-ing there.

(Continued from page 204.)

sermon he wrote: " 'Stand Up For Jesus' was the dying message of the Reverend Dudley A. Tyng, to the Young Men's Christian Association ... The Sabbath before his death he preached in the immense edifice known as Jaynes' Hall, one of the most successful sermons of modern times. Of the five thousand men there assembled, at least one thousand, it was believed were 'the slain of the Lord' ... The following Wednesday, leaving his study for a moment, he went to the barn floor, where a mule was at work on a horse-power, shelling corn. Patting him on the neck, the sleeve of his silk study gown caught in the cogs of the wheel, and his arm was torn out by the roots! His death occurred in a few hours ... The author of the hymn preached from Eph. 6:14, and the above verses were written simply as the concluding exhortation. The superintendent of the Sabbath school had a fly-leaf printed for the children -- a stray copy found its way into a Baptist newspaper, from that paper it has gone ... all over the world."

JOSEPH PHILBRICK WEBSTER

March 22, 1819 - January 18, 1875

Joseph P. Webster, composer of the music for *Sweet By And By,* was born near Manchester, New Hampshire, and by teaching music he earned enough money to enter Pembroke Academy. At the age of twenty-one he went to Boston for further studies. He had a fine baritone voice and played the piano, organ, flute, melodeon and violin. In 1843 he went to New York and sang on the concert stage until 1849, when a severe attack of bronchitis damaged his voice.

In 1857 he moved with his wife and children to Elkhorn, Wisconsin, where he lived for the remainder of his life, composing over a thousand ballads and many beautiful hymns.

SANFORD FILLMORE BENNETT

June 21, 1836 - June 12, 1898

Dr. Sanford Bennett was born in Eden, New York. His family moved to Illinois where he attended the academy at Waukegan and later the University of Michigan. In 1860 he moved to Elkhorn and was associate editor of the Elkhorn *Independent*. During the Civil War he served with the 40th Wisconsin Volunteers. After the war he returned to Elkhorn, opened a drugstore and began the study of medicine.

It is from Dr. Bennett's papers, now the property of The Walworth County Historical Society, that we learn the story of *Sweet By And By:*

"I became associated with Joseph Webster in the production of sheet music and other musical works. In the fall of 1867, we commenced work on *The Signet Ring,* a new Sabbath school book . . . It was a quiet winter afternoon when he came into the drugstore, carrying his violin under his arm. Noticing his rather blue mood, I asked him what was wrong. 'It's not important', he replied. 'It will be all right by and by' . . . It came to me like a flash that this might be an idea for a song . . . The words came like a revelation. It was not I who wrote but something within me . . . When Mr. Webster read the words I had completed, his whole manner changed, his eyes regained their usual sparkle. Stepping . . . to the desk, he began writing the notes. In the meantime, N.H. Carswell, S.E. Bright, and R.R. Crosby had come into the store. After several minutes, Mr. Webster lifted the bow to his violin, and a lovely melody wove its way across the small store into the hearts of the three men standing by" (and eventually Christians everywhere).

Sweet By And By

S. F. Bennett   *J. P. Webster*

1. There's a land that is fair-er than day, And by faith we can
2. We shall sing on that beau-ti-ful shore The mel-o-di-ous
3. To our boun-ti-ful Fa-ther a-bove, We will of-fer our

see it a-far; For the Fa-ther waits o-ver the way, To pre-
songs of the blest, And our spir-its shall sor-row no more, Not a
trib-ute of praise, For the glo-ri-ous gift of His love, And the

Chorus

pare us a dwell-ing-place there. In the sweet by and
sigh for the bless-ing of rest.
bless-ings that hal-low our days.

In the sweet

by, We shall meet on that beau-ti-ful shore; In the
by and by, by and by,

sweet by and by, We shall meet on that beau-ti-ful shore.
In the sweet by and by,

JESSIE BROWN POUNDS

August 31, 1861 - 1921

Born in Hiram, Ohio, Jessie, author of *I Know That My Redeemer Liveth,* began to write for religious magazines when only fifteen years old. And, for over thirty years wrote hymns for James Henry Fillmore, a fellow Disciple and head of Fillmore Brothers Music Company.

At the age of thirty-six Jessie married Reverend John E. Pounds, pastor of the Central Christian Church (Disciples of Christ) in Indianapolis. She was a prolific writer and wrote nine books, fifty cantata librettos and the text of over four hundred hymns.

JAMES HENRY FILLMORE

June 1, 1849 - February 8, 1936

James H. Fillmore, composer of the music to which we sing *I Know That My Redeemer Liveth,* was born in Cincinnati, Ohio, the eldest of seven children. His father was an ordained minister in the Christian Church (Disciples of Christ) as well as an accomplished musician who taught singing, composed music and compiled song books.

James' father died when he was sixteen and to support the family, James took charge of his father's singing school. Later with his brothers he founded Fillmore Brothers Music House. Their first Sunday school book, *Songs Of Glory* (1874), was very successful and thereafter Fillmore Brothers publications became widely used in the Midwest. For the company's many collections, James Fillmore composed a great deal of music, cantatas, anthems and hymn tunes. Many of his tunes were composed for texts supplied by hymn writers as Jessie Pounds with whom he collaborated for thirty years.

I Know That My Redeemer Liveth

Jessie B. Pounds　　　　　　　　　　　　　　　　　　*James H. Fillmore*

1. I know that my Redeemer liv-eth, And on the earth a-gain shall stand;
2. I know His promise never fail-eth, The word He speaks, it can-not die;
3. I know my mansion He prepareth, That where He is there I may be;

1. And on the earth again shall stand;

I know e-ter-nal life He giv-eth, That grace and pow'r are in His hand.
Tho' cruel death my flesh assaileth, Yet I shall see .... Him by and by.
O wondrous tho't, for me He careth, And He at last. ... will come for me.

That grace and pow'r are in His hand.

CHORUS

I know, I know........ that Je-sus liv-eth, And on the
I know, I know

earth........ a-gain shall stand; I know, I know........
And on the earth
I know, I know

that life He giv-eth, That grace and pow'r...... are in His hand.
That grace and pow'r

JAMES ROWE

January 1, 1865 - November 10, 1933

James Rowe, author of *Love Lifted Me,* was born in Devonshire, England. When James was twenty-five years old he came to the United States, married and settled in Albany, New York. He got a job with the railroad and later became superintendent of the Hudson River Humane Society in Albany. His advocation was writing song tests and editing music journals and he was successfully associated with various publishers over the years. His best known hymns are *Love Lifted Me; I Would Be Like Jesus* and *I Walk With The King.*

James Rowe made his home in Wells, Vermont during his later years and with his daughter Louise Rowe Mayhew, a gifted artist, designed and wrote verse for greeting card publishers.

HOWARD E. SMITH

July 16, 1863 - August 13, 1918

Although Howard Smith wrote a number of hymn tunes, including the music for the most loved hymn *Love Lifted Me,* little is known about his life except that he served many years as a church organist in Connecticut and was an active musician throughout his life. We also know that in later years Howard was troubled with arthritis.

James Rowe's daughter gives us this account of the composing of the music for *Love Lifted Me:* "Howard E. Smith was a little man whose hands were so knotted with arthritis that you would wonder how he could use them at all, much less play the piano ... I can see them now, my father striding up and down humming a bar or two and Howard E. playing it and jotting it down ..."

Love Lifted Me

James Rowe   *Howard E. Smith*

1. I was sink-ing deep in sin, Far from the peaceful shore, Ver-y deep-ly
2. All my heart to Him I give, Ev-er to Him I'll cling, In His bless-ed
3. Souls in dan-ger, look a-bove, Je-sus com-plete-ly saves; He will lift you

stained with-in, Sink-ing to rise no more; But the Mas-ter of the sea
pres-ence live, Ev-er His prais-es sing. Love so might-y and so true
by His love Out of the an-gry waves. He's the Mas-ter of the sea,

Heard my despairing cry, From the wa-ters lift-ed me, Now safe am I.
Mer-its my soul's best songs; Faith-ful, lov-ing serv-ice, too, To Him be-longs.
Bil-lows His will o-bey; He your Sav-ior wants to be—Be saved to-day.

CHORUS

Love lift-ed me!.... Love lift-ed me!.... When noth-ing
e-ven me! e-ven me!

else could help, Love lift-ed me. Love lift-ed me.

JEREMIAH EAMES RANKIN

January 2, 1828 - November 28, 1904

J eremiah Rankin was born in Thornton, New Hampshire, and educated at Middlebury College, Vermont. Upon graduation he entered Andover Theological Seminary. He was ordained in 1855 into the Congregational ministry and served briefly in churches in New York, Vermont and Massachusetts before becoming pastor of the Congregational Church in Washington, D.C. in 1869.

It was at Washington that Rankin wrote his famous hymn *God Be With You Till We Meet Again* and then sent the poem to two musicians requesting them to write a tune for it. Rankin selected the tune written by W.G. Tomer, a New Jersey school teacher but his organist at the First Congregational Church, Dr. J.W. Bischoff revised this tune when it was sung for the first time in 1880.

Upon hearing the hymn evangelist Dwight L. Moody adopted it (as did evangelists of many denominations) and soon assemblies of thousands, worldwide, sang with joy the most loved hymn, *God Be With You.*

In 1884 Rankin became pastor of the Valley Congregational Church in Orange, New Jersey, retiring in 1889 to become the president of Howard University in Washington, D.C.

With apologies for the great hymns, composers and histories which had to be omitted, we sincerely hope you enjoyed this trip through history as told through our *One Hundred And One Famous Hymns.*

GOD BE WITH YOU TILL WE MEET AGAIN

Charles Johnson

God Be With You

Jeremiah E. Rankin

William G. Tomer

1. God be with you till we meet a-gain; By His coun-sels guide, up-hold you,
2. God be with you till we meet a-gain; 'Neath His wings protecting hide you,
3. God be with you till we meet a-gain; When life's perils thick confound you,
4. God be with you till we meet a-gain; Keep love's banner floating o'er you,

With His sheep se-cure-ly fold you; God be with you till we meet a-gain.
Dai-ly man-na still pro-vide you; God be with you till we meet a-gain.
Put His arms un-fail-ing round you; God be with you till we meet a-gain.
Smite death's threatening wave before you; God be with you till we meet a-gain.

CHORUS

Till we meet,...... till we meet, Till we meet at Je-sus' feet;
Till we meet, till we meet, till we meet;

Till we meet,...... till we meet, God be with you till we meet a-gain.
Till we meet, till we meet,

213

APPENDIX

Illustrations & Photographs Of Special Interest

Illustrations & Photographs Of Special Interest

Alphabetical List Of Hymns

(Asterisk denotes picture of author and/or composer)

Alphabetical List Of Hymns

(Asterisk denotes picture of author and/or composer)

Alphabetical List Of Hymns

(Asterisk denotes picture of author and/or composer)

Alphabetical List Of Hymns

(Asterisk denotes picture of author and/or composer)

Alphabetical List Of Authors & Composers

(Asterisk next to name denotes photo)

Alphabetical List Of Authors & Composers

(Asterisk next to name denotes photo)

Alphabetical List Of Authors & Composers

(Asterisk next to name denotes photo)

Alphabetical List Of Authors & Composers

(Asterisk next to name denotes photo)

Alphabetical List Of Authors & Composers

(Asterisk next to name denotes photo)

ACKNOWLEDGMENTS

We wish to thank the hundreds of churches, nationwide, who surveyed their congregations to help us select our *One Hundred And One Famous Hymns,* and also the individuals and organizations who then helped us locate the required photographs and biographical information.

UNITED STATES

Colleges and Universities: Dr. John E. Burkhart, McCormick Theological Seminary, Chicago; Rev'd Lundeen, Lutheran School of Theology, Chicago; Diana Yount, Special Collections Librarian, Andover Newton Theological School, Newton Centre, Mass.; Union Theological Seminary, New York; Evelyn Gibson, Director of Public Information, Biola College, La Mirada, Calif.; Karl Kabelac, Assistant Librarian, The University of Rochester Library, N.Y.; Owen D. Nichols, Vice President for Administration, Howard University, Washington, D.C.; Christina H. Kavanaugh, Assist. Director of Alumni Relations, Widener College, Chester, PA; John Dick, Media Relations Coordinator, Moody Bible Institute, Chicago.

Historical Societies: Russell L. Young, Jr., Admin. Secretary, World Methodist Council, Lake Junaluska, N.C.; Louise L. Queen, Admin. Assistant, Commission on Archives and History, The United Methodist Church, Lake Junaluska, N.C.; Gerald W. Gillette, Research Historian, The Presbyterian Historical Society, Philadelphia, PA; Rev'd Edward C. Starr, Curator, The American Baptist Historical Society, Rochester, N.Y.; Marvin D. Williams, Jr., Director of the Library and Archivist, Disciples of Christ Historical Society, Nashville, Tenn.; Harold L. Myers, Assoc. Historian, Commonwealth of Pennsylvania, Pennsylvania Historical and Museum Commission, Harrisburg, PA; Bill Copeley, Assist. Librarian, New Hampshire Historical Society, Concord, N.H.; Isabel S. Pide, Treasurer, Rush County Historical Society, Rushville, IN ; Mrs. Helen Kluge and Fred Young, curators, Walworth County Historical Society, Elkhorn, WI.

Churches: Rev'd & Mrs. M.R. Hinds, The Little Brown Church In The Vale, Nashua, Iowa; Rev'd Richard L. Francis, John Street United

ACKNOWLEDGEMENTS

Methodist Church, New York, NY; Rev'd Robert G. Withers, The First Baptist Church In America, Providence, R.I.; Rev'd Floyd LaBombard, First Baptist Church of Bennington, VT; Christ Church, Boston, Mass.; Rev'd John A. McConomy, Augustus Lutheran Church, Trappe, PA; Beatrice M. Loennecke, Exec. Secretary and Registrar, Plymouth Church Of The Pilgrims Brooklyn, N.Y.; Dorothy Reynolds, Secretary to the Rector,; Saint Thomas Church, New York, N.Y.; Mrs. H.A. Jensen, Historian, First Congregational Church, Minneapolis, MN; Malcolm Rigby, Church Archivist, First Congregational United Church of Christ, Washington, D.C.; Ruth L. Boyd, Office Secretary, First Congregational Church, Bath, Maine; Rev'd Alec J. Langford, Central Christian Church, Indianapolis, IN; Rev'd Homer L. Trickett, The First-Park Baptist Church, Plainfield, N.J.; Rev'd H. Edward Whitaker, Emmanuel Baptist Church, Brooklyn, N.Y.; Rev'd Dana McLean Greeley, First Parish Church, Concord, Mass.; Cleo Render, Office Manager, The First Congregational Church, Columbus, Ohio; Ada M. Bass, Publications Office, The Riverside Church, New York, N.Y.; Rev'd Irving R. Phillips, First Presbyterian Church, Lansing, MI; Rev'd Donald L. Dixon, Petersburg Baptist Church, Petersburg, N.Y.; Marion M. Brooks, Chairman, Trinity Church, Boston, Mass.; Rev'd D. Owen Brubaker, Pine Street United Methodist Church, Williamsport, PA.

Other: Mrs. C. Thomas Malbon, Greenfield, Mass.; A.L. Wildzumas, Menands, N.Y.; Anna L. Park, Town Clerk, Chamber of Commerce, Wells, VT; Dr. Earl Marlatt, Winchester, IN; Mrs. David Dahlstrom, Reed City, MI; Ulf C.E. Lundberg, Admin., The United Methodist Homes Of New Jersey, Ocean Grove, N.J.; Judy Busse, Secretary, The United Methodist Homes Of New Jersey, Ocean Grove, N.J.; Miss Martha Mussina, Williamsport, PA; Mrs. Charles E. Hofer, Public Relations, Pennsylvania Chamber of Commerce, Harrisburg, PA; Greg McMahon, Manager, Port Hope Chamber of Commerce, Ontario, Canada; J. Vincent Higginson, The Hymn Society Of America, New York, NY;

ENGLAND

Universities and Government Agencies: Ms Cornelia Starks, Secretary, Bodleian Library, Oxford University, Oxford; Cambridge University; Nathalie McCance, Assist. Keeper of the Portraits, Royal College Of Music, London; J. Hutton, Chief Clerk, University of Durham, Old Shire Hall, Durham; Francis W. Steer, Archives, New College, Oxford; I.R. Wright, Keeper of the Records, Queens' College, Cambridge; J.E. Silke, Registrar, Somerset College of Arts and Technology, Somersetshire; Rev'd Kenneth Twinn, Secretary & Librarian, Dr. Williams's Library, London; Miss J. Prendaergast, Publications Assist., National Portrait Gallery,

ACKNOWLEDGEMENTS

London; J.A. Parkinson, Senior Research Assistant, The British Library, Music Library, London; J.G. Morgan-Owen, Vice Judge Advocate General, Judge Advocate's Office, London; John W. Bamford, City Treasurer, City Hall of Westminster, London; J.P. Henry, Publishing and Information Officer, Borough of Trafford, Stretford; Eileen Allen, Secretary, Sidmouth Town Council, Sidmouth; G.A. Knights, Manager, William Clowes & Sons Limited, Suffolk;

Churches: Rev'd N. Allen Birtwhistle, John Wesley's Chapel, London; Rev'd Wilfrid J. Little, John Wesley's Chapel, Bristol; Rev'd David H. Bishop, Church of England, Council for Places of Worship, London; Rev'd Kenneth N.J. Loveless, former Dean of Hackney, London; Rev'd John Clingo, Vicar, Monkland, Herefordshire; Rev'd John Hester, Vicar of Brighton, East Sussex; S.W. Shackleton, Secretary, Hope Baptist Church, Hebden Bridge; Rev'd K.E. Jackson, Lew Trenchard Church, Devonshire; Rev'd E. Downing, Vicar, Shareshill, Wolverhampton, Staffordshire; Rev'd C.A. Rowe, Vicar, St. Matthias, London; Rev'd Cyril H. Grant, Redland Park United Reformed Church, Bristol; Rev'd B.G. Burr, Vicar, Brixham and Churston Ferrers; Anne Yelland, Secretary, All Saints' Church, Brixham; S. Piggott, Secretary, Rehoboth Free Grace Baptist Chapel, Horsham, Sussex; M. Price, Secretary, Guild Church of St. Mary Woolnoth, London; Rev'd Derek Strange, Christ Church, Uxbridge, Middlesex; Arthur E. Barker, Archivist and Librarian, Holy Trinity Church, London; Rev'd Brian L. Golland, The General Assembly of Unitarian and Free Christian Churches, London; The Reverend Mother Superior C.H.F., Holmhurst St. Mary, East Sussex; and The Hymn Society of Great Britain and Ireland.

Wales: Deys S. Webb. Glam, S. Wales; P. Davies, Principal, Memorial College, Abertawe, Swansea.

Scotland: Rev'd George A. Young, St. Bernard's Parish Church, Edinburgh; George Knox, Director, Ettrick and Lauderdale District Council, Galashiels.

Ireland: Rev'd G.F. Good, Dean of Derry, Londonderry; G.M. Geary, Town Clerk, Londonderry City Council, Londonderry.

Switzerland: Rev'd Jornod, General Secretary, St. Pierre's Church, Geneva; E.O. Bötschi, Deputy Consul General, Consulate General of Switzerland, Chicago.

Germany: Rev'd Grüben Herzlich, St. Nicholas Church, Obendorf; Director of Lutherhalle, Wittenberg.

Israel: Mayor Kollek, Municipality of Jerusalem; Anna Grace Vester Lind, Director, Spafford Children's Center, Jerusalem; Noemi Teasdale, Secretary, The Mayor's Office, Jerusalem; Daphna Avnon, Admin. Director, The Jerusalem International Book Fair, Jerusalem; M. Levin, Jerusalem Historical Archivea.

BIBLIOGRAPHY

Benson, Louis F. *The Hymnody of the Christian Church.* Richmond: John Knox Press, 1956.

Bucke, Emory Stevens (ed.) *Companion to the Hymnal*, a handbook to the 1964 Methodist Hymnal. Nashville: Abingdon Press, 1970.

Covert, William Chalmers (ed.) *Handbook to The Hymnal.* Chicago: Presbyterian Board of Christian Education, 1935.

Dole, Nathan Haskell. *Famous Composers.* New York: Thomas Y. Crowell & Company, 1902.

Emurian, Ernest K. *Famous Stories of Inspiring Hymns.* Boston: W.A. Wilde Company, Publishers, 1956.

Emurian, Ernest K. *Sing the Wondrous Story.* Natick: W.A. Wilde Company, 1963.

Encyclopedia of World Methodism. 2 vols. Nashville: Abingdon, 1974.

Garland, Henry James, *Henry Francis Lyte and The Story of Abide With Me.* London: Torch Publishing Company.

Haeussler, Armin. *The Story of Our Hymns, The Handbook to the Hymnal of the Evangelical and Reformed Church. Missouri: The General Synod of the Evangelical and Reformed Church, 1952.*

Hart, William J. *Unfamiliar Stories of Familiar Hymns.* Boston: W.A. Wilde Company, 1940.

Historical Companion to Hymns Ancient & Modern Wm. Clowes & Sons, London, 1962.

Lövgren, Oscar. *Lina Sandell.* Stockholm: Gummessons Bokförlag, 1965.

MacDougall, Hamilton C. *Early New England Psalmody.* Brattleboro: Stephen Daye Press, 1940.

Martin, Hugh (ed.) *The Baptist Hymn Book Companion.* London: Psalms and Hymns Trust, 1962.

McQuere, Kenneth G. *Music of Moody.* Chicago: Moody Bible Inst. 1976.

Northcott, Cecil. *Hymns We Love.* London: Lutterworth Press, 1954.

Parry, K.L. and Erik Routley. *Companion to Congregational Praise.* London: Independent Press Ltd., 1953.

Polack, W.G. *The Handbook to the Lutheran Hymnal.* Saint Louis: Concordia Publishing House, 1942.

BIBLIOGRAPHY

Reese, Gustave. *Music in the Renaissance.* New York: W.W. Norton & Company, 1959.

Reynolds, William Jensen. *A Survey of Christian Hymnody.* New York: Holt, Rinehart and Winston, Inc. 1963.

Reynolds, William Jensen. *Hymns of Our Faith*, A Handbook For The Baptist Hymnal. Nashville: Broadman Press, 1964.

Rudin, Cecilia Margaret. *Stories of Hymns We Love.* Chicago: John Rudin & Company, Inc., 1946.

Ryden, E.E. *The Story of Christian Hymnody.* Rock Island: Augustana Book Concern, 1959.

Sanville, George W. *Forty Gospel Hymn Stories.* Winona Lake: The Rodeheaver-Hall Mack Co., 1945.

Scholes, Percy A. *The Oxford Companion To Music.* London: Oxford University Press, 1943.

Stevenson, Robert. *Protestant Church Music In America.* New York: W.W. Norton & Company, Inc., 1966.

The Dictionary of Welsh Biography, London: 1959.

The Hymnal 1940 Companion. New York: The Church Pension Fund, 1949.

Thulin, Oskar (ed.). *A Life Of Luther.* Philadelphia: Fortress Press, 1966

The World Book Encyclopedia. 8 vols. Chicago: Field Enterprises, Inc., 1950.

Pamphlets

A Short Life of Phillips Brooks, William Lawrence

All Saints' Church, Brixham, England, B.G. Skinner

Bread Of Life, Vol. 23 No. 4, Ridgewood Pentecostal Church, NY

Bucknell World, Vol. 3 No. 5 & 6, Bucknell University, PA.

Bruton Parish Church, Williamsburg, VA, Parke S. Rouse, Jr.

Letters of John Newton, The Banner Of Truth Trust, London

History of Dauphin County, (Penn.), biographies, John Wyeth

Hope Baptist Church 1858 - 1958, Hebden Bridge, England

Joseph Scriven, Kiwanis Club of Port Hope, Ontario, Canada

New Room, People And Places In Early Methodism, Book Three, Maldwyn Edwards

Old Meeting Congregational Church, Uxbridge, 1662 - 1962, K. Pearce

150 Years of a New Town Church, St. Bernard's Parish, Edinburgh

150-Year History of First-Park Baptist Church of Plainfield, N.J.

The Hymn Society of Great Britain and Ireland, Bulletin 135 Vol. 8

The Meeting House Of The First Baptist Church In America, R.I.

The Old North Church, 250 years, Boston, Massachusetts

The Webster House, Walworth County Historical Society, Elkhorn, WI.